Macrobiotic Child Care
and Family Health

D1598050

MACROBIOTIC
CHILD CARE
and
FAMILY HEALTH

by Michio and Aveline Kushi

Edited by Edward and Wendy Esko

Japan Publications, Inc.

Photo credits: pp. 31, 42, 44, 47, 51, 75 (bottom), 76, 77, 81, 87, 91, 105, 106, 108, 111, 116, 118, 119, 205—Lars Host Rasmussen; pp. 36, 43, 64 (bottom), 75 (top), 82, 85, 86, 113, 115, 117 (top), 120 (top)—Alain Ando Hirsch; pp. 53, 118 (bottom)—Alain Ando Hirsch/East West Foundation; p. 60—Alain Ando Hirsch/Macrobiotic Children's Gathering; pp. 19, 34, 46, 64 (top), 94, 102, 106, 134—Yoshio and Veronique Kushi; pp. 66, 67, 69, 129, 212—Mari Kennedy; pp. 117 (bottom), 120 (bottom), 122—Adelbert Nelissen; pp. 11, 127, 130—Michael Maloney; p. 65—Julie M. Fischer; p. 58—East West Foundation; p. 121—Andrea Harnick; p. 195—Steve Levine.

Note to the reader: It is advisable to seek the guidance of a qualified health professional and macrobiotic counselor before implementing the dietary and other suggestions for specific conditions presented in this book. It is essential that any reader who has any reason to suspect serious illness in themselves or their family members seek appropriate advice promptly. Neither this or any other book should be used as a substitute for qualified care or treatment.

Published by JAPAN PUBLICATIONS, INC., Tokyo and New York

Distributors:
UNITED STATES: *Kodansha International/USA, Ltd., through Harper & Row, Publishers, Inc., 10 East 53rd Street, New York, New York 10022.* SOUTH AMERICA: *Harper & Row, Publishers, Inc., International Department.* CANADA: *Fitzhenry & Whiteside Ltd., 195 Allstate Parkway, Markham, Ontario, L3R 4T8.* MEXICO AND CENTRAL AMERICA: *HARLA S. A. de C. V. Apartado 30–546, Mexico 4, D. F.* BRITISH ISLES: *International Book Distributors Ltd., 66 Wood Lane End, Hemel Hempstead, Herts HP2 4RG.* EUROPEAN CONTINENT: *Fleetbooks, S. A., c/o Feffer and Simons (Nederland) B. V., 61 Strijkviertel 3454 PK De Meern, The Netherlands.* AUSTRALIA AND NEW ZEALAND: *Bookwise International, 1 Jeanes Street, Beverley, South Australia 5007.* THE FAR EAST AND JAPAN: *Japan Publications Trading Co., Ltd., 1–2–1, Sarugaku-cho, Chiyoda-ku, Tokyo 101.*

First edition: June 1986

ISBN 0–87040–612–4
LCCC No. 84–081357

Printed in U.S.A.

Foreword

Growing up macrobiotically has been an experience shared by few. While attending public schools in New York City, the Greater Boston area and Los Angeles, I was always acutely aware of the differences between the food my family would have at home and the lunches served in the school cafeterias or brought to school by my classmates. These differences were further highlighted when I visited my friends' homes. While we might snack on brown rice or noodles with vegetables at our house, they would have sandwiches of baloney on white bread, or store-bought cookies and crackers.

It does not take much imagination to envision the difficulties these dietary differences could have on young children who strive for acceptance among their peers. We often hear of the social pressure involved when adolescents experiment with their first cigarette, or beer. Important as these experiences are for socialization, they generally represent a minor part of daily life. Food and food choices, on the other hand, are an integral part of human existence, and the obvious differences in this area between my family and others was a continued source of anxiety.

Early in my elementary school days, my parents would prepare rice balls *(omusubi)* for my siblings and I to take to school for lunch. I remember clearly how they would be made—of brown rice, flavored with a touch of *umeboshi* and covered with *nori* sea vegetable. They were then wrapped in aluminum foil and placed in the paper bags we carried to school. Had we lived in Japan, such lunches would have been common; one can purchase similar lunches (though made with white rice and *umeboshi* with food coloring) on the "bullet" trains that run from Tokyo to Osaka, and elsewhere throughout Japan. Even in Gay Head on Martha's Vineyard, where we attended school for a few months, these lunches were accepted, with some curiosity, by our classmates. On one occasion, my mother prepared such rice balls for all fifteen of the pupils who attended our one-room schoolhouse. They were a great hit.

Outside of such rare experiences, however, the usual reaction to these rice balls was negative and critical. "What's that?" my classmates would ask. In response to my explanations, they would contort their faces and exclaim, "Yeech, seaweed! How can you eat that stuff?" They would then watch with horrified fascination as I would self-consciously try to eat my lunch. It was not much help that the teachers would have similar reactions, though without the caustic remarks. But it was not difficult to detect a mixture of concern and fascination in their observations of the food I was eating. Thinking back on those experiences, I wonder if those people know that every bite of commercial ice cream they eat contains some of that infamous "seaweed."

My eventual response to such experiences was to stop bringing lunch to school. I developed the habit of sitting and socializing with my friends, but not eating, during lunch periods. After school, I would return home for a mid-afternoon meal. Initially, this did little to allay my teachers' concerns, since all they could see was that one of their pupils was not eating lunch. However, they came to accept that as part of my lifestyle. This was not without incident, however. The very first day I attended elementary school in Brookline, Massachusetts, I did not have a lunch, having already developed the habit of not eating at school. Nor did I wish to purchase the school lunch (they were serving hot dogs). My teacher was concerned, not having encountered such a situation before, and failing to understand my reluctance to buy lunch in the cafeteria. In final frustration, the school's principal was called in to deal with this unique situation. She marched down from her office and forced me to stand in line for lunch at her side. I cried tears for sympathy, and acquiesced to their demands by somehow managing to be served peanut butter in a hot dog roll (minus the hot dog, of course).

The other side of this experience was that I did "experiment" with the food that makes up the mainstream American diet. Clandestine favorites included Snickers bars and peanut M&M's. I luxuriated in the cool, smooth mouth-feel of vanilla ice cream with jimmies. I tasted bananas for the first time at a high school graduation pot-luck party, and pineapples when I was off on my own in college. I discovered the therapeutic value of late night discussions—and parties—fueled in part by mushroom pizzas. These foods, that were not available at home, were the illicit drugs of my youth. I did draw the line of experimentation at red meat (which I have knowingly tasted three times in my life—twice by accident), poultry (which I have yet to consume knowingly), and artificial sweeteners such as cyclamates or saccharin (which I may have unknowingly eaten).

The first realization I had that macrobiotics reached beyond my family's immediate experience came early in ninth grade, when someone in my history class, whom I did not know, mentioned macrobiotics. This was the first time I met someone who knew of macrobiotics in a context outside my family's network of friends and acquaintances—truly a historic moment. Soon afterward, I discovered that my English teacher frequented the Seventh Inn restaurant, which my parents had just recently opened, and my history teacher shopped regularly at Erewhon, a natural foods store owned by my parents.

Eventually, these discoveries became so commonplace that, in college, I was sometimes sought out because of my experience with macrobiotics. An example of the growing acceptance of alternative eating patterns was the vegetarian dining option at the college I attended. Out of a population of about 1,400 students, 150 to 200 would choose the vegetarian meal during any given evening. While many of these students ate "vegetarian" simply because the usual fare was less appetizing, a substantial proportion was dedicated to this lifestyle. Although other students at the college deserve the credit for organizing and overseeing the vegetarian dining hall, I did play a small role in influencing the food choices that were available. Partly through my suggestion, the college decided to order some food items from

Erewhon, and the head chef at the Seventh Inn restaurant volunteered his time so he could demonstrate, to the kitchen staff at the college, preparation methods for brown rice, *miso* soup and simple steamed or sautéed vegetables.

You, the readers of this book, are probably parents of children, parents-to-be, or former parents. As you adopt a macrobiotic lifestyle, your concerns may include the consequences of such a change for your children—for their health, their socialization, their overall well-being. Although each family and child is unique, some words of encouragement and advice can apply broadly. This book can be a source of such advice, as well as of common sense suggestions for dealing with specific situations.

Elements of my youth and adolescence probably strike chords of familiarity with your and your children's experiences. At a recent macrobiotic summer camp, one teenager remarked that, with his macrobiotic practice, he had felt like a real outcast among his friends, and had not until then understood the significance of macrobiotics for him. In a society where the vast majority of people have little dietary consciousness, such feelings can be common for children who are raised in the minority of families who do care about the quality of their food.

Solutions to this type of problem are as varied as the families that wrestle with it. Some have attempted to create communities where all families share the same philosophy of life, so that the social circles the children grow and play in do not have the conflict of experience familiar to my siblings and I. Others have attempted to accomplish the same goals by simply refusing to send their children to public—or private—schools, even if this deprived their children of playmates within their age group. Another approach is exemplified by the mother who has made a point of taking each of her children to McDonald's and other bastions of the American diet, so they would experience those foods and not feel any guilt about eating them. The former approach might be characterized as a "search for utopia," while the latter might be thought of as a "promotion of the inevitable."

In the United States of the 1980s, promoting macrobiotic dietary habits in the face of social pressures is much easier than it was fifteen or twenty years ago. Many of the foods that are an integral part of macrobiotic practice have only recently become widely available. Basic items such as organically grown whole grains, beans and seeds could not be had when I attended elementary school. The only whole grains one could readily purchase in food stores were oatmeal, wheatena, and shredded wheat cereal. Brown rice was sold as a gourmet item at some stores, but the price was a few dollars a pound. My family sometimes shopped for sesame and sunflower seeds at pet stores, where they were sold as feed for parakeets and canaries.

The availability of many of the food items that many of us now take for granted can be directly traced to people such as Paul Hawken, one of the first presidents of Erewhon, who took it upon himself to search out farmers who would be willing to grow organic rice. His and my parents' commitment to developing such sources of good quality food by guaranteeing purchase of these crops even before they were planted was instrumental in creating our current food supply. Dotted throughout the countryside are organic farms, small *tofu* and *tempeh* producers, and sometimes bakers of good sourdough bread. Almost all major cities in this country, and most of western Europe, have outlets that sell good quality whole grains and fresh vegetables. In some of these cities, such as Boston, Los Angeles or Minneapolis, many of these food items are sold in the supermarkets. Some of these cities also have restaurants that cater primarily to people interested in macrobiotics, serving little if any red meat, poultry or dairy food, and including such menu items as bean or sea vegetable of the day. We can be grateful for all of the heralded and unheralded people responsible for these and other related accomplishments.

All these recent developments can only serve to ease the acceptability of your child's macrobiotic eating habits to his or her peers. My nephew was recently attending the same elementary school where I ate my first—and only—peanut butter "hot dog." At least two of the teachers there have been interested in macrobiotics, and several of the other children who attend the school are from macrobiotic families. With these small but significant changes in society, concern about protecting children from dietary extremes, or of how to deal with awkward social situations, start to diminish. Rather than searching for utopia or promoting the inevitable, there can be a middle ground.

As I reflect on the experiences my parents must have gone through, with five of us children, I sometimes wonder what their thoughts might have been about these situations. I doubt that I or any of my siblings could have secretly munched on ice cream or Oreo cookies without their knowing of it, as we thought we were doing at the time. Yet, I do not recall one incident when my parents punished me, or became hysterical, for my eating outside the "borders" of macrobiotic practice. While this may have been because my older siblings bore the brunt of punishment, and they tired of dealing with it when my turn to experiment came, I suspect it had more to do with their philosophy of life. Obviously, my parents did not attempt to create a utopia where we would be shielded from the temptations of society. Neither did they push us to experience as many gustatory bombs and delights as we could. What they did do was create for us a home environment that was as comfortable and "macrobiotic" as possible. Many of the food items, such as dairy food or tropical fruits, that are occasionally found in some macrobiotic households, would seldom if ever be seen at our house. My parents never prevented us from trying other foods, though they would be quick to point out the relationship between our physical health and the food we had recently eaten. Fevers, stomachaches, swollen lips or runny noses could all be traced to recent patterns of eating or specific food items.

Many people who come to macrobiotics also seem to be concerned about implications for their children's health. High among these concerns is the possibility of various nutrient deficiencies. Does a macrobiotic diet provide enough protein, calcium, or vitamin B_{12}? These questions are especially acute for those with infants and children, as it is the practical responsibility of parents to ensure the health of their young children. During his lectures, my father sometimes proudly proclaims that none of his children have been hospitalized, except for birth, or have taken any medications for sickness. By and large, this apparently miraculous feat in this age of medicalization is true. I was admitted overnight to a hospital once, for observation after I suffered a concussion and was somewhat amnesiac. I also did take aspirin once, and penicillin once, when I developed some sort of gastro-intestinal upset when I was in South Asia. Otherwise, his tale is true for me, and probably similarly so for my siblings.

Such experience notwithstanding, it is important to realize that following a standard macrobiotic diet does require a bit more knowledge about nutrition than simply following the four food groups. I am aware of infants who have been hospitalized for vitamin B_{12} difficiency whose parents have been faithful, perhaps too much so—such that their diets were too narrow or rigid—in their practice of macrobiotics. I am also aware of other macrobiotic infants with cases of calorie malnutrition and vitamin D deficiency (rickets) that may have resulted from similar practices. Although these cases have been few, their occurrence is reason enough for increased levels of awareness about diet and nutrition. These cases also serve as evidence that such increased awareness can be beneficial.

There is sometimes a tendency for people in macrobiotics to ignore such warnings, believing that following macrobiotics in a dogmatic way will ensure freedom from illness. In its extreme, this tendency can lead to individuals closing their minds to such seemingly negative experiences, dismissing them as cases in which the people involved "obviously didn't know how to practice macrobiotics." A case in point is the experience of some students at the Kushi Institute that was recounted to me recently. One of the instructors spent part of his class discussing the possibility of vitamin deficiencies. The students then proceeded directly to another class, in which the instructor told them, "One of the other teachers here is spreading rumors of nutrient deficiencies in the macrobiotic community. Don't you believe a word of it!" Although one might argue from a practical and public relations standpoint of the advisability of discussing nutrient deficiencies with students learning macro-biotics, it is clearly simplistic to dismiss the possibility altogether. Indeed such dismissal is contrary to the curiosity and search for understanding that is the macrobiotic spirit.

Generally, the way to raise healthy children, as is mentioned throughout this book, is to follow your intuition and use common sense. The best barometer of your infant's or child's well-being is your observations of his or her growth, physically, mentally and spiritually. Does he or she react quickly to different stimuli? Does it seem that he or she is growing and developing with a natural inquisitiveness and explorer's heart? Watch for infants who are overly quiet (oh, how well-behaved he is!) or extremely aggressive. And of course, do not be afraid to seek out opinions about the health of your children from others, within and without the macrobiotic community. In your search for information, it can be useful to follow the advice of many health care practitioners: Take charge, be on top of things, be voracious in your appetite for knowledge, and do not ever give away your freedom to choose. In short, take responsibility for your children's lives until they are able to take responsibility themselves.

It is important to keep these health and illness concerns in perspective, recognizing that occurrences of nutrient deficiencies are few. Advice about some of these concerns are contained within these pages. Otherwise, it bears mentioning that it is best to eat a variety of foods, as much a cliche as that may be. And, use some common sense instead of following recommendations blindly. Although soy milk may look like breast milk, and have similar organoleptic properties, the two are not nutritionally equivalent. *Kokoh* is also not similar to breast milk, and neither *kokoh* nor soy milk should be used as a sole source of infant nutrition. While trying not to foster a "food as nutrients" perception, it can be helpful to incorporate into your diet beans, bean products and sea vegetables on a daily or every-other-day basis. Please eat fish if you desire, and do not feel guilt over an occasional dietary transgression. Much more importantly, use macrobiotics as a basis for enjoying life, of discovering the infinite variety of experience that unfolds daily around us and within us.

More representative of the norm for macrobiotic children are the comments often heard at macrobiotic summer camps. At these gatherings, hardly a day or hour goes by that someone does not remark how beautiful and bright the children are, and how healthy and inquisitive they appear. As a father of one and an uncle of four, I can readily appreciate these comments, and be grateful that I know of macrobiotics, for myself and for the children in my life. I am certain that my brothers and sister would echo these sentiments. Although we all drifted away from macrobiotic "practice" at some point and to some extent in our lives, we have all returned to the spirit of macrobiotics, in our diet, our way of life, and our commitment to a better world. Indeed, we never left that spirit, being nourished by our parents' quiet example and spiritual guidance. I am truly grateful to them, for the experiences that being their son has brought.

The adventure that is macrobiotics can be infinitely rewarding, providing life with great insights and unsolvable enigmas. Those of us with children have the additional benefit of a shared adventure. Children can help us reflect on our lifestyles, appreciate our ancestors, and experience further dimensions of the human condition. While periods of anxiety and worry occur as part of the rhythm of life, these can also be turned around to become opportunities for self-reflection and growth. This book can assist you as a guidepost to help you understand and pass through some of these periods that are a part of family life. Please enjoy these pages, and accept, adapt or reject the thoughts and practices they bring to you. Most of all, pursue your dreams so that your own and your children's development can reach its fullest potential.

In Peace,
LAWRENCE HARUO KUSHI, SC. D.
Minneapolis, Minnesota
September, 1985

A Word from Aveline

It was not until I read my son Haruo's foreword to this book that I realized the extent to which our children were on the frontier of the introduction of macrobiotics to society. The macrobiotic movement was very small in the America of the 1960s. During these early years I spent most of my time at home attending to the children and teaching cooking classes to small groups of students and friends. I was not very active in introducing macrobiotics outside of the small circle of friends who came to our home. Haruo's foreword made me realize that I probably could have gotten more involved in the children's outside activities and put more time and energy into creating macrobiotic dishes that their friends could identify with.

Fortunately, all of our children have been very supportive and have shared in their parents' dream of health and peace for society. They are all living macrobiotically, and are now raising their own children this way as well. I am continuously grateful to them.

I have always had a great interest in the education of children, but when I arrived in America, I spoke very little English. When my children started school, my lack of English prevented me from taking an active role in their schooling.

As I look back on the children's experiences with the public schools, I can think of several areas where parents could participate in making positive changes. Food was always a major issue when the children were in school. When Haruo went to Amherst college, I worried that he would have trouble eating macrobiotically. At first I thought we would have to rent a house in Amherst and ask one of our friends to prepare meals. Then I decided to approach the school administration. To my surprise, the college was happy to set up a vegetarian café. Surprisingly, about 120 students signed up for vegetarian meals. I gave the staff basic advice on the preparation of natural foods, and asked a chef from one of Boston's macrobiotic restaurants to show them how to prepare brown rice, *miso* soup, and other dishes.

Now, several years later, my youngest son, Hisao, attends college in the same area. He has had no problems eating well or finding high quality foods. Many colleges now have vegetarian menus for their students and faculty. I would like to encourage parents to take an active role in improving the food situation in their children's schools.

Making the best quality food available for our children is of course essential for their future health and well-being. But the quality of education needs to be considered as well. Children deserve the very best education to prepare them to carry the world into a bright future.

Before the Second World War, education in Japan was based on a more traditional model. I graduated from teacher's college around that time and taught elementary school before coming to America. The most important principle of education was not teaching children to memorize facts and figures, but rather guiding them in the development of a well rounded personality. This included the ability to judge and figure things out for themselves, the capacity to love others and to relate to a wide variety of people and to society at large, and the willingness to assume responsibility for their health and their behavior. Helping a child develop as a whole person is far more important than providing information to remember. If their overall personality remains undeveloped, children will not be equipped for adult life.

In Japan, the teaching of self-development was known as *Shūshin*. When I went to school we would spend time each week reading and studying the classics, history, and the lives of great people in both East and West as a part of our self-training. More recently, however, Japanese education has become completely modern, and the teaching of *Shūshin* has been abandoned. At the same time, school cafeterias now serve modern meals, and the more traditional diet that went along with the teaching of *Shūshin* has also been abandoned.

In the future, I hope that education will again include such practical training to help children develop as whole persons, rather than offering only technical training. A more holistic approach to education is vital if children are to be able to relate to all of humanity and contribute in the future to world peace. Parents and teachers can cooperate in adding this aspect to the education of children.

Happily, parents and schools are beginning to become aware of the importance of food. In Belgium, for example, sugar and foods that contain it are not served in the schools. This constructive step came as the result of the influence of our many macrobiotic friends there. In Brookline, macrobiotic parents have joined with other concerned parents to lobby for better nutrition. Several elementary schools have included brown rice, *tofu*, and other whole natural foods in their menus.

In the future, I hope that all public institutions, and especially schools will discover how important our daily food is in creating health and happiness. Childhood is the foundation for future life, and should be something that everyone looks back on with happy memories. Making each child's school experience healthful and rewarding is an important element in this. One of the goals of macrobiotics is to make the highest quality education available for our children. In this way, we can make a direct contribution to a healthy and peaceful world in the future.

AVELINE KUSHI
Brookline, Massachusetts
November, 1985

Acknowledgments

We would like to thank all of our friends who helped in the creation of this book. We thank Edward and Wendy Esko, our friends and associates for many years, for compiling and editing our seminar materials in book form, and for adding insights based on years of macrobiotic practice, teaching, and experience with their five wonderful children.

We wish to thank our son, Lawrence Haruo Kushi, now at the University of Minnesota, for writing the foreword, and for his ongoing research in the area of diet, health, and nutrition.

We also thank the friends who took the delightful photographs of macrobiotic children. The bright, happy, and energetic children in these pictures are typical of macrobiotic children around the world. The pictures convey the spirit of child care much more effectively than do words. We thank Lars Host Rasmussen, the award winning Danish photographer, for his patient efforts, together with Alain Ando Hirsch, Mari Kennedy, Yoshio and Veronique Kushi, Adelbert Nelissen, Julie Fischer, Andrea Harnick, and Michael Maloney. These charming and inspiring photographs were taken in Brookline, Stockbridge, and Becket, Massachusetts, as well as in Philadelphia, Holland, and at the annual macrobiotic summer camp for children—the Becket Children's Gathering—in the beautiful Berkshire mountains of western Massachusetts.

We thank our friends who contributed the diagrams and illustrations. We thank Peter and Bonnie Harris for their charts and diagrams, and Christian Gautier for his sensitive drawings.

We also thank Flo Nakamura for her help in typing the manuscript, and Phillip Jannetta and other members of the Japan Publications staff in Tokyo for editing and proofreading the text. We deeply appreciate the patience, guidance, and inspiration offered by Mr. Iwao Yoshizaki and Mr. Yoshiro Fujiwara, respectively president and New York representative of Japan Publications, Inc.

We thank our children and their spouses—Lilian, Norio and Lori, Haruo and Gabriel, Yoshio and Veronique, and Hisao; together with our grandchildren—Yogen, Tenji, Angelica, Lianna, and Takeo. We also appreciate the thousands of macrobiotic families with children around the world. They inspire us with hope for a bright and happy future in which all people may enjoy one peaceful world.

MICHIO and AVELINE KUSHI

Contents

Chapter 1

Family Health and Happiness

The family is humanity's oldest and most natural institution. It is a miniature version of the order of life itself. The family is the place where human life comes into physical being, where it is loved and nourished, and where it receives the orientation for sound physical, mental and spiritual growth. Long before the ancient civilizations of Sumer, Egypt, and China flourished, the family provided the thread from which the fabric of human culture was woven.

The family has survived repeated natural catastrophes and the rise and fall of countless civilizations. Of all our social structures, it has proven to be the most durable and flexible. It is an often overlooked fact that strong and healthy families are the cornerstone of a healthy and prosperous society. When the family is strong, so is society and the individuals that comprise it. When the family becomes weak, society as a whole begins to suffer.

There is no reason why the family cannot continue indefinitely, as long as the earth is capable of sustaining human life. However, of all the challenges—both natural and man-made—that the family has met and adjusted to during its long history, perhaps none are as great as those which confront it at this point in history. The very continuation of the family as we know it is now being challenged on many fronts, and as a consequence, civilization itself is in danger of degenerating.

The decline of the family in the twentieth century is often attributed to economic and social changes that occurred as a result of the industrial revolution. During the later part of the nineteenth century, for example, millions of people left their ancestral homelands and migrated to the rapidly industrializing cities. Until about 1920, the majority of Americans lived in rural areas. Just 60 years later, however, in 1980, more than 80 percent of the population were living in cities.

This mass migration is associated with the decline of the *extended family*—in which three or four generations plus assorted relatives live together in the same house, farm, or village—and the rise of the *nuclear family*, with a husband, wife and children forming the central unit. In the nuclear family, grandparents or other relatives usually do not live in the same house or meet daily with their children, grandchildren, or kin. Contact with relatives outside the nuclear family is often very limited.

One of the few groups today who have kept the extended family alive is the Amish of Pennsylvania. The Amish believe that relatives "should live close enough to see the smoke from each other's chimneys." The extended family is also strong among people in Asia, Africa, Latin America, and other less industrialized parts of the world. Even with industrialization, the extended family is still strong in Japan, although recently it has begun to weaken there also.

In modern America, however, even immediate family members are often separated by thousands of miles. In such cases, phone calls, letters, and occasional visits cannot substitute for the benefits of daily interaction. Aged parents are frequently sent to retirement communities or nursing homes rather than being invited to live with their grown children. This practice is recent, and contrasts markedly with traditional expressions of respect and gratitude toward parents and elders, including the desire to care for them under any circumstances.

The extended and nuclear families represent opposite poles of family life. While the extended family emphasizes the place of the individual within the larger unit and cooperation for the common good, the nuclear family is identified more with the pursuit of individuality, often without consideration for, or in some cases, at the expense of, the larger family unit. With a rural agricultural base, the extended family tended more toward production and self-sufficiency. Children were viewed as contributing to the overall productivity and prosperity of the family as a whole. A large family was considered a sign of wealth.

The nuclear family, on the other hand, is oriented more toward consumption and dependence on others. From a consumerist point of view, children are often seen as liabilities. Couples often feel the need to limit the number of children or hesitate to have any at all because of economic considerations. An extreme result of this thinking is the trend toward zero growth and low fertility rates among married couples. Some of the complementary tendencies of the traditional extended family and the modern nuclear family are summarized in the table below.

Table 1 General Tendencies: The Extended and Nuclear Family

Characteristic	Extended Family	Nuclear Family
Period	Pre-industrial	Industrial
Environment	Rural	Urban
Lifestyle	Agricultural	Industrial
Orientation	Time	Space
	Tradition	Fashion
	Unity	Fragmentation
	Solidarity	Individuality
Reproductive Ability	Toward increased fertility	Toward diminished fertility
Tendency	Toward stability, integration, and growth	Toward instability, dissolution, and decay
Economic Function	Production	Consumption
	Self-sufficiency	Dependency
Outlook	Cooperative	Competitive
	Spiritual	Materialistic
	Intuitive	Analytical

These tendencies are of course relative and interchangeable. Some extended families embody characteristics of nuclear families and vice versa, while people within each type of family frequently have differing tendencies.

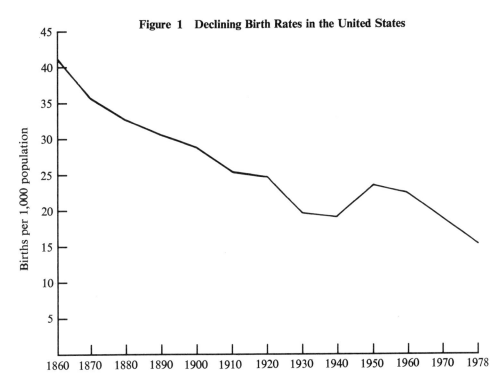

Figure 1   Declining Birth Rates in the United States

Births per 1,000 population

Sources: U.S. Bureau of the Census, *Current Population Reports*, 1965; *Recent Social and Economic Trends*, 1979.

The development of industrial technology, the migration to the cities, and the rise of the nuclear family occurred together with another profound change in the nature of family life. While these changes were occurring on the surface, more fundamental biological changes were taking place at a deeper level. As people moved to the cities, they abandoned not only their rural agricultural lifestyle, but their more traditional, natural diet as well. In East and West, North and South, since the beginning of civilization, families nourished themselves with whole cereal grains, beans, fresh local vegetables, and other products of their regional agriculture. From the pioneer families who crossed the Great Plains to the Imperial Household of Japan, whole cereal grains and other complex carbohydrate foods were revered as staple items in the diet. Countless families throughout history sat down to eat with the prayer, ". . . give us this day our daily bread."

However, from 1910 to 1976, during which time the divorce rate increased nearly 700 percent, the per capita consumption of wheat fell 48 percent, corn 85 percent, barley 66 percent, buckwheat 98 percent, rye 78 percent, beans and legumes 46 percent, fresh vegetables 23 percent, and fresh fruit 33 percent, according to calculations based on U.S. Department of Agriculture surveys. During the same period, in which the average number of children per family dropped by half, beef intake rose 72 percent, poultry 194 percent, cheese 322 percent, canned vegetables 320 percent, frozen vegetables 1,650 percent, processed fruit 556 percent, ice cream 852 percent, yogurt 300 percent, corn syrup 761 percent, and soft drinks 2,638 percent. The consumption of chemical additives and preservatives is also recent; the amount of artificial food colorings added to the diet increased 995 percent since 1940, the first year that records were kept.

During this century, the emphasis shifted from a diet based more on the complex carbohydrates found in whole grains, beans, and vegetables, to a diet centered around animal protein, fat, and refined carbohydrates. At the same time, naturally fertile plant and animal species were replaced by infertile, artificially fertilized, or, more recently, genetically manipulated species. The vast majority of eggs now consumed in the United States, for instance, are unfertilized, while 95 percent of the beef cattle are now produced through artificial insemination. Many species of plants—including cereal grains—have been genetically manipulated to conform to modern agriculture and marketing practices.

Not only are the types of foods on the family dinner table different, but so is the place where they are eaten. Until the middle of the twentieth century, people usually ate at home, together with their families. In the early part of the century, restaurants were found mostly in the larger cities and tended to cater to a small urban clientele. However, according to John C. Maxwell, Jr., writing in *Advertising Age*, by 1965, the average American ate about one meal in four outside the home. By 1973, one in three meals were eaten in restaurants or cafeterias. It is now estimated that during the 1980s, Americans will eat an average of one meal in two away from home. Fewer families eat together as their parents, grandparents, and ancestors once did. The trend toward taking meals away from home parallels the decline of the extended family and the decomposition of the family in general.

Table 2   The Extended and Nuclear Family: Differences in Dietary Patterns

Extended Family	Nuclear Family
Centered around complex carbohydrates (whole grains, beans, vegetables, etc.)	Centered around protein, fat and refined carbohydrates
Whole	Processed
Natural	Artificial
Organic	Chemical
Unrefined	Refined
Locally grown	Transcontinental
Seasonal	Nonseasonal
Prepared and eaten at home	Prepared and eaten outside the home
Influenced by tradition	Influenced by advertising
Naturally fertile plant and animal species	Infertile, artificially conceived, or genetically manipulated species

The twentieth century model of the nuclear family, in which a working husband supports a wife and two or more children reached its zenith in the middle of this century. However, it too is now in the process of disappearing, and currently makes up a minority of the households in the United States. In addition, a growing percentage of families are headed by a single parent, most often a woman. There are now about nine million *single parent households* in the United States. About a third of all American children will be brought up in single parent families during the 1990s.

Figure 2   Children Aged Eighteen and Under Living in Single Parent Households, 1960 and 1978

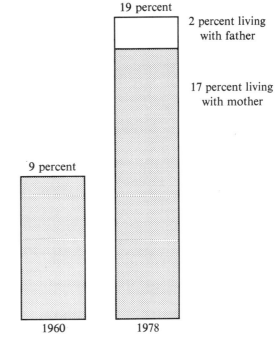

19 percent

2 percent living with father

17 percent living with mother

9 percent

Source: "Future American Families," by P.C. Glick, *Coalition of Family Organizations Memo*, Summer/Fall, 1979.

1960   1978

The number of people living alone is also increasing rapidly. *Single person households* totaled fewer than 10 percent of all families in the 1950s. By 1984, nearly a quarter of all households were made up of people living alone. Like single parent families, the number of single person households is expected to increase in the years to come.

If current fertility trends are not reversed, the twenty-first century could witness the dawn of the *artificial family*, in which children are produced through artificial insemination, in-vitro fertilization, or other artificial techniques due to the decline of reproductive ability. The genetic engineering of the human species could also become widespread. If this "Brave New World" scenario comes to pass, it could mean the end of the family as we think of it, and consequently, the extinction of the natural human species.

Table 3   Divorce Rates in the United States

Year	Number of divorces	Divorces per 1,000 population
1900	55,751	0.7
1910	83,045	0.9
1920	170,505	1.6
1930	195,961	1.6
1940	264,000	2.0
1950	385,144	2.6
1960	393,000	2.2
1970	715,000	3.5
1975	1,026,000	4.8
1976	1,077,000	5.0
1977	1,091,000	5.1
1978	1,122,000	5.1
1979	1,170,000	5.3

Sources: Various reports of the U.S. Department of Health and Human Services and National Center for Health Statistics.

Food Unites the Family

In the past, family life centered around the hearth or kitchen where food was prepared and served. A wife or mother would put her time, energy, and love into making delicious and nourishing meals for her family. Mealtime was the time when the family would meet and discuss the day's events, resolve problems, make plans for the future, and share love, warmth, and good spirit. Mealtimes also offered a wife or mother the opportunity to observe the members of her family. Based on her observations, she could adjust her cooking and selection of foods on the following day to meet their changing conditions.

A woman recreates her image in the food that she cooks. When a man eats food prepared by his wife, his daily physical and mental condition are created by her. Both his sperm quality and the quality of her reproductive cells are created by the food that they share. Then, when the couple has intercourse, the woman receives sperm, the quality of which she helped to create. If she becomes pregnant, she then nourishes not only herself and her husband, but her baby as well. Her emotions, thoughts, and dreams affect the baby both directly and through the influence they have on her cooking. After giving birth, she then nourishes her baby with her milk, the quality of which is also directly influenced by her cooking and emotions. After weaning her baby, she prepares baby food and then children's food, and may cook for her children until they leave home many years later. Children who are raised in this manner naturally experience a strong physical, emotional, and spiritual bond with their mothers, fathers, and other members of their families.

Today, however, this natural pattern is frequently disrupted. Consider the case of John and Mary, a fictional couple who we can use to highlight the conditions of many couples today. Mary has an active career outside the home and is too busy to cook. Because she frequently works late, she usually stops for dinner at a restaurant near the office. The dinner chef is overweight and suffers from diabetes and high blood pressure. He works at the restaurant not so much because he enjoys cooking or out of love for the customers, but simply because he needs to earn a living.

The chef's physical and emotional condition directly affects the quality of the food he prepares. He frequently becomes upset and tends to handle the food in a rough, sloppy manner. As she eats there so often, Mary has surrendered her biological quality to an unknown chef. Because his food influences the condition of her blood, and through it her entire body, this chef is actually the hidden director of her life.

John has also gotten into the habit of stopping off at a diner on his way home from work. A female cook usually works in the kitchen during the dinner shift. Like the chef, she is overweight and suffers from a variety of physical and emotional problems. She is not particularly fond of cooking. Since her shift begins early in the morning, she is usually exhausted by the time John comes in for dinner. Because John eats there so often, his physical and emotional conditions are greatly influenced by her temperament and state of health.

The quality of this couple's reproductive cells—John's sperm and Mary's egg—is influenced not by Mary, but by these restaurant cooks. When their reproductive cells combine and a baby begins to develop, the male chef continues to have a decisive influence on the unborn child, since Mary keeps working and eating at a restaurant until just before delivery.

When John Jr. is born, rather than nursing the baby herself, Mary chooses an infant formula. As soon as he is old enough, she begins feeding him factory-processed baby foods. The restaurant chefs are as much the child's biological parents as John and Mary are, while the stepparents are the cows who provide milk for the infant formula and the factories where the processed baby foods are manufactured.

As soon as John Jr. is old enough, he is dropped off at a day-care center and introduced to the world of institutional and fast foods.[1] It is rare for the family to eat at home with everyone present. Since John and Mary, and John Jr. eat separately more often than together, they do not feel love for each other. They often quarrel and, like many couples, the parents eventually divorce. As John Jr. grows older, he begins to feel closer to his friends who join him at the fast food restaurant or in the school cafeteria than he does to his parents. He spends more time in front of the television than he does with either parent. As he grows older, communication and understanding become increasingly difficult. Like many other children, John Jr. begins to feel isolated from his parents. He may consider running away from home, or he may decide to strike out on his own as soon as he is old enough.

When children brought up this way begin their own families, they often do so independently of their parents. They may move to another city and visit parents only on holidays or special occasions. When the parents retire, their children may send them to an old age home, retirement community, or some other institution rather than care for them in their own homes. As we can see, the patterns of isolation begun in childhood often last throughout life, so that sadly, many people today finish their lives alone, abandoned by their families and loved ones.

Although imaginary, the story above resembles the lifestyle of many modern families, and indicates the path down which numerous other families are headed. Although simplified, it underlines the direct and decisive influence that daily food has on physical health and emotional and mental orientation. Clearly, the well-being of individual family members determines the quality of a family's life together.

The factors that produce a healthy, well-balanced life will be our next topic of discussion.

Recovering Family Health

What distinguishes a family from society as a whole? Once it was understood that the members of a family had a similar quality of blood, hence expressions such as "bloodline" and "blood relatives" came into being. These expressions symbolize the fact that the members of a family share a quality that is unique and distinct from that of other families and individuals in society.

Where do blood and biological quality come from? Daily food and drink are the primary factors in the creation of blood, body fluids, and cell quality. Families are united because their members share the same or a similar quality of food. When the members of a family eat differently, they lose their underlying unity

---

[1] *Child Care in the United States:* An increasing number of children today are being cared for outside the home, usually by persons other than the parents. According to the U.S. Census Bureau, more than 50 percent of the pre-school age children of full-time working mothers are cared for at group day-care centers, at someone else's home, or at the place where the mother works.

even if they share the same living space. The result is fragmentation, isolation, and a breakdown in communication and understanding. The members of a family begin to think and act without a common dream and understanding. If the desires of individual members clash, disagreements, quarrels, and arguments come to characterize family relations.

The first step in restoring harmony to the family is to begin eating together. However, simply eating together is not enough. If people eat poor quality foods, or if their diets are excessive or inadequate, they risk the eventual decomposition of their family due to cancer, heart disease, or some other degenerative sickness.

Family disharmony frequently begins with disharmony between a husband and wife. Sexual disharmony, frustration, and unhappiness are the frequent cause of conflict among couples and thus are at the root of many family problems. Love and sex are the natural means to create offspring. Love and sexual attraction result from the complementary natures of men and women. The male reproductive organs, for example, are complementary to those of the female. The ovaries, Fallopian tubes, and uterus are held deep within the body in an upward position. The testes, scrotum, and penis have a more downward position outside the body.

These differences are reflections of the two complementary energies that produce and animate all things on earth. Although the bodies of both males and females are charged by these two energies, there is a difference in their degree of intensity between the sexes. In the male body, descending, centripetal forces that come from the cosmos predominate. These include stellar, solar and galactic radiation, cosmic particles, solar and galactic winds, and a variety of high frequency waves. In the female body, rising, centrifugal forces generated by the earth's rotation are stronger. Hence the classical association of paternal or masculine energy with heaven and maternal or feminine power with the earth.

The forces of heaven and earth continuously supply the body with life energy and animate all of its functions. The rhythms of the body—sleeping and waking, appetite and fullness, sexual desire and satisfaction, movement and rest, and the expansion and contraction of the heart, lungs, stomach and digestive organs— reflect the alternating pulse of these primary energies.

A man and a woman exchange these energies during intercourse. Orgasm is similar to the spark of lightning that passes between the atmosphere and the ground during a thunderstorm. The buildup of excessive energy is neutralized in a flash of lightning. Similarly, a man's excessive charge of heaven's energy and a woman's excessive charge of earth's energy are momentarily neutralized when they unite during intercourse.

If the exchange of energy is smooth, both partners enjoy a healthy sex life and a mutually satisfying relationship. Naturally, they then relate to each other and to their children in a more loving and flexible manner. In order for a relationship to work smoothly, however, the couple's physical quality needs to be compatible. If they dine separately, and if their eating habits are chaotic, their physical and mental qualities become dissimilar. A husband and wife may become so unlike each other, in fact, that they may feel they are living with a stranger. In such a case, the couple's energy and biological qualities no longer match.

Diet also affects sexuality in another important way. When a husband or wife eats excess amounts of cheese, milk, butter, eggs, meat, poultry and other foods containing heavy, saturated fats, their bodies begin to lose their natural conductivity to environmental energies. Deposits of hard fat begin to form in the arteries, blood vessels, and in and around the organs. The tissues themselves become more rigid and inflexible, and the skin becomes hard, tough, and insensitive. Nine out of ten adults have this condition to one degree or another. It can be diagnosed simply by lying on your back with your knees raised and feet flat on the floor. Slowly breathe out and push your lower abdomen deeply but gently with the extended fingers of both hands. If you feel hardness or tightness here, or if you feel pain, the tissues in this region have already become tight and hard. Hardness or rigidity in the abdominal region is practically universal among adults. This condition interferes with the normal flow of environmental energies throughout the body, particularly in the region of the sexual organs.

Tightness or stiffness in the muscles and joints and hardening of the blood vessels accompany abdominal hardening. They are the result of a diet rich in cholesterol and hard, saturated fats, together with the consumption of foods such as refined sugar, tropical fruits, and oily or greasy dishes. Love and sexuality depend on our sensitivity to environmental energies, including the energy of our partner. If our body becomes hard and inflexible, our sensitivity, and therefore our sexuality and capacity to love diminishes.

Dietary imbalances can directly hamper the normal functioning of the reproductive organs. In men, for example, the excessive intake of fatty, oily or greasy foods, together with the overconsumption of protein, especially from animal sources, causes excess to build up in the prostate gland. The first signs of accumulation are often small microscopic nodules, known as *prostatic concretions*, that appear in the more alkaline fluid secreted by the gland. If plenty of hard fats are consumed—especially those contained in cheese, butter, ice cream and other dairy products—and iced or chilled foods or drinks are taken frequently, the concretions may harden and calcify in a manner similar to the formation of kidney stones. Prostatic concretions may accumulate in the tissue of the gland in the form of cysts.

In many cases, the accumulation of fats and other types of excess causes the prostate to enlarge. Enlargement is further aggravated by the intake of sugar, alcohol, tropical fruits, honey, fruit juice, coffee, spices, and drugs and medications. *Benign prostatic enlargement* has become nearly universal among men: it is estimated that 10 percent have some form of enlargement by the age of forty and practically 100 percent experience it by the age of sixty. Enlargement of the prostate produces a variety of symptoms including difficulty in starting the flow of urine, dribbling of urine after urination, and increased frequency of urination, especially at night.

The *prostate gland* has a compact and tight structure and is located below the bladder. It surrounds the *urethra*, the tube that conveys sperm and urine to the outside via the penis. It also surrounds the *ejaculatory ducts* through which sperm travel en route to the urethra. During ejaculation, the prostate contracts and aids

in the transport of the seminal fluid. As we can see, the prostate is directly connected to male sexual functioning. If it becomes swollen, enlarged, or filled with
calcified cysts, sexual ability and enjoyment decrease. Many cases of impotence,
unsatisfactory sexual relations, or diminished vitality can be traced to problems
in the prostate gland. (The relationship between diet and female reproductive disorders is discussed in detail in our other family health book, *Macrobiotic Pregnancy
and Care of the Newborn.*)

Physical hardness and rigidity lead to a variety of psychological problems, including feelings of separateness from one's environment and from friends and family.
Children, and especially babies, do not usually experience these feelings. They
normally sense that they are very much a part of what is going on around them.
This is because their physical conditions are soft and flexible, thus allowing the
unrestricted flow of energy through their bodies. This healthy conductivity to environmental forces creates the relatively high rate of physical and mental activity
found in children. Flexibility in body and mind is associated with such positive
attributes as imagination, creativity, playfulness, open-mindedness, explorativeness,
resiliency, optimism, and honesty.

Feelings of isolation from one's social and physical surroundings usually begin
after childhood, as stagnation and hardness begin to appear in the body. As our
physical condition becomes more rigid, our thinking and outlook come to reflect
this change. Creativity and originality are replaced by imitation and lack of
imagination. Instead of being open-minded and full of curiosity, our outlook
becomes narrow and closed to new ideas, while optimism and honesty may change
into negativity and habitual repression of our thoughts and feelings. All too often,
love and warmth are replaced by coldness and detachment.

Physical and mental inflexibility cause expression to become increasingly harsh
and critical. A more peaceful, gentle or subtle manner of expressing ourselves is
difficult when our physical condition becomes hard and inflexible. In such cases,
even when we wish to show love or affection, our expression often takes the form of
criticism, scolding, or belittling others. Frustration builds as we lose the ability to
freely express ourselves through words, actions, or creativity. Frustrations can only
be pent up for so long before they erupt destructively, especially when they are
fueled by an unbalanced diet.

Abusive behavior is occurring widely between husbands and wives, and parents
and children. All too often, the dinner table, traditionally a place of togetherness
and love, becomes a battleground, with loud and abusive behavior being served as
the main course. The relationship between diet, physical condition, and abuse and
neglect is summarized below in Table 4.

The problems that confront the family today—from divorce and child abuse to
infertility and juvenile delinquency—can be traced directly to individual imbalances
in daily diet, mental attitude, and way of life. In the following sections, we introduce a simple, common sense approach to health for the whole family through
balanced diet, a natural daily life, and the recovery of love and understanding. By
creating healthy and happy families, we are planting the seeds of peace and prosperity for generations to come.

Table 4 The Relationship between Diet, Physical Health, and Abuse and Neglect

Type of Abuse or Neglect	Related Emotional Disturbance	Related Organ Dysfunction	Primary Influences (when consumed excessively)	Secondary Influences
Physical Abuse: A sudden outburst of anger in which a parent strikes or hits a child, sometimes producing injury.	anger, short temper, impatience	liver and gallbladder	meat, poultry, eggs, red meat or blue-skinned fish, oil, fat	sugar, alcohol, drugs, medications, hard salty cheese, salt, chemical additives, pesticides, air pollution, overeating, lack of exercise, lack of outlet for creative expression
Verbal Abuse: Shouting, screaming, or talking to children in an offensive or hysterical manner.	excitability, excessive talking or laughing, shouting, feelings of "stress"	heart and small intestine	saturated fats, dairy, sugar, spices, tropical fruits, alcohol, coffee, fruit juice	meat, eggs, poultry, insufficient activity, lack of discipline in daily life, chemicals, drugs, medications
Calculated Abuse or Neglect: Punishments such as locking a child in a dark room or tying a child to a bed; scolding or belittling a child; abandonment of children.	irritability, suspicion, cynicism, lack of warmth or kindness	spleen, pancreas, and stomach	milk and other dairy, sugar, oil, fat, soft drinks, chemicals	animal food, poultry, eggs, spices, radiation, lack of contact with nature, tropical fruits and vegetables, stimulants, drugs, medications, insufficient mental stimulation
Passive Neglect: Failure to protect a child's physical welfare, for example by disregarding avoidable hazards in the home or leaving children under the care of an inexperienced person; failure to properly dress, clothe, or feed a child; lack of concern about children.	depression, sadness, frustration, extreme self-centeredness, laziness	lungs and large intestine	dairy, oil, fat, sugar, white flour, animal food	flour products, fruit, spices, coffee, baked foods, alcohol, excessive fluid, soft drinks, air pollution, overeating, eating prior to sleeping, insufficient physical activity, isolation from society
Sexual Abuse	fear, insecurity, depression	kidneys, bladder, and endocrine glands	fats, oil, meat, dairy, sugar, soft drinks, alcohol, coffee, excess fluid in general	salt, cold or iced foods or beverages, fruit, chemicals, drugs, medications, insufficient activity, social or physical isolation
Multiple Abuse or Neglect				any combination of the above

Food for Healthy Families

It is important for families to eat together, as we have seen. But if members share poor quality food, the family will eventually experience physical and mental disorders, and ultimate decomposition. To secure the long term health and well-being of the entire family, we recommend basing the family's daily diet around such natural and traditional foods as whole cereal grains, fresh local vegetables, beans and bean products, and other complex carbohydrates. When animal foods are desired, white-meat fish and other low-fat seafoods may be eaten occasionally. The foods that your family is served can have a deliciously natural flavor without strong spices or artificial seasonings. Cereal grains, beans, and vegetables such as carrots, squash, *daikon* (long white radish), and cabbage are all naturally sweet, and can be emphasized in cooking. Natural seasonings such as sea salt, *tamari* soy sauce (*shoyu*), *miso* (fermented soybean paste), *umeboshi* plum (salted pickled plum), and others can be used moderately to create genuinely flavorful dishes and to bring out the original sweetness of your foods.

We recommend that all members of the family eat macrobiotically. However, the general suggestions that follow are not meant to be used rigidly or interpreted dogmatically. Everyone has different needs based on factors such as their age, sex, type of activity, physical constitution, present condition, and other characteristics. Children's dietary needs are especially different from those of adults. For example, parents need to pay careful attention to the amount of salt that their children use. Grown-ups can generally use a larger—but not excessive—volume, while it is better for babies and small children to avoid salt entirely, at least during the first year or so. The seasonings and condiments that are recommended for moderate daily use can be introduced gradually as children grow. Milder condiments can be prepared for children until they are grown.

Please always keep the uniqueness of each child in mind. As an aid in judging the particular needs of a child, mothers can reflect on their own dietary practices and experiences during each pregnancy. This will help when making adjustments for individual children. Since children's needs and desires differ from those of adults, the proportions outlined in the standard macrobiotic way of eating can be modified at each stage in the developmental process. General suggestions for adjusting the standard recommendations for children are discussed below and in Chapter Three. Dietary suggestions for common childhood illnesses are presented in Chapter Four. Specific recipes are presented in the *Recipe and Home Care Guide* in Chapter Five.[2] Recommendations for adjusting your cooking for the older members of your family, including the elderly, are included below. For additional suggestions and information, we recommend contacting a qualified macrobiotic instructor.

Our diets also need to be adjusted in response to the changing conditions in the environment, for example, varying from season to season and from climate to climate. General recommendations for modifying the standard macrobiotic way of eating to suit particular environments are included in our other books listed in the Bibliography. These books are also recommended for further study. In general, an optimally balanced diet in a temperate, or four-season, climate consists of the following proportions of food:

1. *Whole Cereal Grains*

We recommend that cooked whole grain cereals comprise at least half (50 percent) of every meal. Cooked whole grains are preferable to flour products as they are easier to digest. *Whole grains for daily use include:* Brown rice (short grain is preferable in temperate climates), millet, barley, corn, whole oats, wheat berries, and rye. *Whole grains for occasional use include:* Sweet brown rice, *mochi* (pounded sweet brown rice), whole wheat noodles (including *udon* and *somen*), buckwheat, buckwheat noodles (*soba*), unleavened whole wheat or rye bread, or unleavened bread made from other whole grains, rice cakes, cracked wheat, bulgur, steel cut and rolled oats, corn grits and meal, rye flakes, and couscous. In general, it is better to keep the intake of flour products, flaked cereals, and products such as couscous and grits below 20 percent of the daily proportion of whole grains.

---

[2] Additional suggestions for preparing a variety of children's foods are presented in *Macrobiotic Family Favorites* by Aveline Kushi and Wendy Esko, Japan Publications, Inc., 1986.

Figure 3 The Standard Macrobiotic Diet

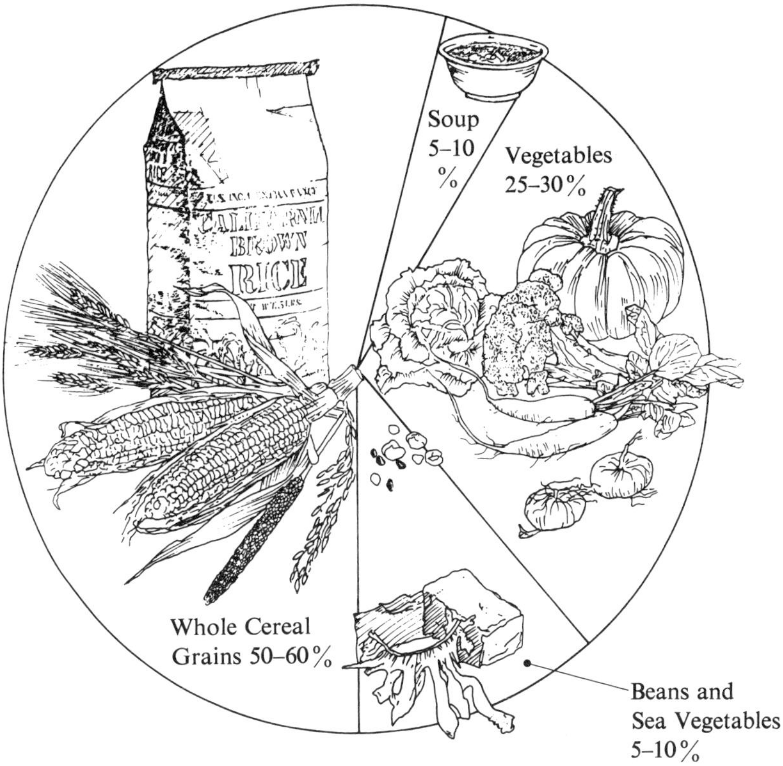

Plus Supplementary Foods

Whole grains are normally the first solid foods for babies. When making cereals for infants and small children, use more water than you normally do for adults.

If children are under the age of one, it is better to cook their grains with no salt; a one-inch piece of *kombu* can be used instead. If they are under two, a very small amount of sea salt (several grains of salt for one or two cups of grain) can be added. Adults can use condiments to adjust the flavor of their grain dishes. Children may also like to have condiments. If so, condiments can be made from plain roasted seeds, such as sesame or sunflower, or very mild sea vegetable and sesame seed condiments, omitting the use of salt when necessary.

2. *Soups*

One or two cups or small bowls of soup may be included daily. We recommend seasoning soups with a moderate amount of miso, tamari soy sauce, or sea salt, so that they taste neither too salty nor too bland. Soups may be prepared with a variety of ingredients including seasonal vegetables, sea vegetables—especially *wakame* and kombu—and grains and beans. Barley miso, also known as *mugi* miso, is generally better for regular use, while soybean (*Hatcho*) and brown rice (*genmai*) miso may be used on occasion.

Babies can have simple, unseasoned vegetable broth soups. Before seasoning the adult soup with sea salt, miso, or tamari, remove a small portion of the unseasoned broth and vegetables for babies. For older children, remove their broth and season it very lightly. After removing the children's portion, season the remaining broth to taste for the adults in the family. Children usually do not like garnishes such as parsley or scallions in their soups. A piece of cooked green vegetable or a few strips of toasted *nori* sea vegetable can be used instead. Soups may be introduced after about six to eight months.

3. *Vegetables*

About one-quarter (25–30 percent) of each meal may include vegetables prepared in a variety of ways, including steaming, boiling, pressure-cooking and others. In general, up to one-third of your daily vegetable intake may be eaten in the form of macrobiotically prepared pickles or salad. We recommend avoiding commercial dressings and mayonnaise.

When cooking vegetables for young children, use the same technique that you do with soups. Remove their portion before adding sea salt or other salty adult seasonings. After removing your children's vegetables from the cooking pot, place them in another pot and, when necessary, let them cook a little longer, as children's vegetables need to be softer than those eaten by adults. Older children can eat adult-style vegetables. Boiled salads can be cooked a little longer for children. When using *nishime* style, or "waterless" cooking, vegetables can be prepared with kombu instead of salt for babies. Children over two can have very mild seasoning in their nishime dishes. Vegetables can be introduced when teeth start to come in, usually after the baby has been eating grains for about a month.

Vegetables for regular use include:[3]

1) *Stem/root vegetables:* Burdock*, carrots, daikon, dandelion root*, lotus root*, onion, radish, rutabaga*, turnip, and parsnip.
2) *Ground vegetables:* Cauliflower, acorn, buttercup, butternut, and Hubbard squash, Hokkaido pumpkin, and pumpkin.
3) *Green and white leafy vegetables:* Broccoli, Brussels sprouts, bok choy, green cabbage, carrot tops, Chinese cabbage, collard greens, daikon greens, dandelion greens, kale, mustard greens*, parsley, scallion*, chives*, turnip greens, watercress, and leeks*.

Vegetables for occasional use include: Celery, cucumber, endive, escarole, mushroom, romaine lettuce, *shiitake* mushroom (a mushroom native to Japan), sprouts, kohlrabi, iceberg lettuce, green peas, snow peas, summer squash, pattypan squash, string beans, snap beans, wax or yellow beans, *jinenjo** (mountain potato), and red cabbage.

Vegetables to avoid include: Asparagus, bamboo shoots, fennel, ferns, spinach, okra, purslane, sheperd's purse, sorrel, avocado, eggplant, green and red peppers, tomato, potato, sweet potato, taro (albi), plantain, yams, zucchini, and Swiss chard.

4. *Beans, Bean Products, and Sea Vegetables*
About 5 to 10 percent of your daily diet may include cooked beans, bean products, and sea vegetables. *Beans for regular use include:* Azuki beans (small red bean), chick-peas, and lentils. *Beans for occasional use include:* Black-eyed peas, black turtle beans, black soybeans, kidney beans, great northern beans, whole dried peas, split peas, pinto beans, lima beans, and navy beans. Fermented bean products such as *tempeh* (an Indonesian fermented soybean product), *tofu* (soybean curd), dried tofu, and *natto* (fermented soybeans) may also be included on a regular basis. (Naturally processed whole wheat products like *seitan* [seasoned wheat gluten] and *fu* [dried wheat gluten] may also be used in various side dishes from time to time.)

Children do not need to eat beans until they are about two years old, although a small volume can be introduced earlier. It is difficult for babies to digest beans.

Children under two can have tofu, dried tofu, and tempeh. These can be introduced after ten months. Cook thoroughly, use little or no seasoning, and serve in small amounts. When beans are introduced, be sure to cook them until they are quite soft. The cooked beans can then be mashed and given in small amounts to your children. Tofu and tempeh can be introduced around the age of ten months.

We suggest that sea vegetables be eaten everyday, so that they comprise about 5 percent of daily intake. Sea vegetables can be prepared in a variety of ways,

[3] The starred vegetables are generally not recommended for babies. Their flavor is generally too strong for small children, and children often refuse to eat them. Sweeter tasting vegetables are preferable for small children. Small amounts of the stronger flavored vegetables may be introduced after one-and-a-half years, although some children take longer to adjust to them.

for example in soups, with beans (kombu is especially recommended), or as side dishes with vegetables, such as carrots or onions, or with the soybean products mentioned above. *Sea vegetables for regular use include:* Kombu (for soup stocks, as a side dish, or in condiments), wakame (in soups—especially miso soup—as a side dish, or in condiments), nori (as a garnish, a condiment, or in rice balls), *hijiki* (as a side dish), *arame* (as a side dish), dulse, Irish moss, agar agar (for gelatin molds), and *mekabu* (as a side dish).

Adults can enjoy more strongly seasoned sea vegetable dishes. Children may have very mildly seasoned or unseasoned sea vegetables. Their sea vegetables can be cooked until they are very soft. Babies under a year do not need any seasoning, so simply cook the sea vegetables until they become very soft. Senior citizens may also enjoy sea vegetables that are mildly seasoned and cooked until they become very soft. Sea vegetable side dishes—such as those with hijiki or arame—can be introduced after a baby is one-and-a-half to two years old, although wakame, kombu, nori, and other varieties can be used in the preparation of other dishes or for occasional consumption from the first introduction of solid foods.

5. *Supplementary Foods*
Depending upon age, condition and type of activity, a small amount of white-meat fish or seafood may be eaten once or twice a week. *Suitable varieties include:* Flounder, halibut, sole, carp, haddock, trout, clams, oysters, smelt, scallops, shrimp, *chirimen iriko* (tiny dried fish), and *chuba* (small dried fish).

Fish is generally not necessary as a regular part of a baby's diet.

A small volume of roasted seeds, lightly seasoned with sea salt or tamari, may be

enjoyed as snacks by adults and older children. *Suitable varieties include:* Sesame, sunflower, pumpkin, and squash seeds.

It is better to minimize the use of nuts and nut butters as they are high in fats and often difficult to digest. However, less oily nuts such as almonds, walnuts, and chestnuts may be enjoyed on occasion by adults and older children, preferably roasted and lightly seasoned with tamari or sea salt.

Desserts may be enjoyed now and then, generally about two to three times per week. Unsweetened, cooked fruit desserts are preferable. However, small amounts of high quality natural grain sweeteners such as rice syrup, barley malt, or *amazaké* (slightly fermented sweet brown rice) may be added occasionally. Dried and fresh local fruits in season may also be enjoyed from time to time by those in good health. The regular consumption of fruit juice is not recommended, although it may be enjoyed periodically by those in good health, including children, especially during warm weather. Only locally grown fruits are advisable; therefore, it is better for persons living in temperate climates to avoid tropical and semi-tropical fruits and their products.

Fruit desserts are not necessary until after a child is one year old. It is important to note that small children and the elderly should not eat desserts that make them cold, such as *kanten* or chilled custards. It is better in such cases to serve room temperature or warm desserts. Children should also avoid eating too many desserts made with a lot of oil or flour.

Recommended sweets include:

1) *Sweet vegetables:* Cabbage, carrots, daikon, onion, parsnip, pumpkin, and squash.
2) *Concentrated sweeteners (in small amounts):* Rice syrup (often referred to as *amé* or yinnie syrup), barley malt, amazaké, chestnuts, apple juice, raisins, apple cider, and dried, temperate climate fruits.
3) *Temperate climate fruits:* Apples, strawberries, cherries, blueberries, watermelon, cantaloupe, peaches, plums, raspberries, pears, apricots, and grapes.

6. *Beverages*

It is recommended that spring or well water be used in the preparation of teas and other beverages. *Beverages for daily use include:* Bancha twig tea *(kukicha)*, bancha stem tea, roasted rice tea, roasted barley tea, boiled water, and spring or well water. *Beverages for occasional use include:* Grain coffee, dandelion tea, kombu tea, umeboshi tea, and *Mu* tea (a tea made from a variety of herbs). *Beverages for use occasionally in moderate amounts only include:* Nachi green tea, green magma, vegetable juices, temperate climate fruit juice (apple juice or cider, unsweetened, is preferable), beer, and *saké* (rice wine).

It is better to drink as thirst requires rather than out of habit. Babies may use spring or well water that has been boiled and cooled to room temperature, bancha twig tea, cereal grain teas, apple juice (preferably warmed or hot), and amazaké that has been boiled with twice as much water and then cooled.

7. *Condiments*

Condiments may be used in moderate amounts to add a variety of flavors to foods and to provide additional nutrients. Please remember that these condiments contain salt or minerals. Adults and older children can use them in moderation. Infants and small children need not use them. Please refer to Chapter Three for recommendations for introducing condiments to children.

The following condiments may be used by adults and older children:

- *Tamari soy sauce:* Use mostly in cooking. Please refrain from using tamari on rice or vegetables at the table.
- *Sesame salt (Gomashio):* For adults, use ten to fourteen parts sesame seeds to one part roasted sea salt. (When making gomashio for children, use a larger proportion of sesame seeds.) Wash and dry-roast seeds. Grind seeds together with sea salt in a small earthenware bowl called a *suribachi* (a serrated clay bowl), until about two-thirds of the seeds are crushed.
- *Roasted sea vegetable powder:* Use either wakame, kombu, dulse or kelp. Roast the sea vegetable in an oven until crisp (approximately 350°F. for 10 to 15 minutes) and crush in a suribachi.
- *Sesame seed powder:* Use four to eight parts sesame seeds to one part roasted sea vegetable (kombu or wakame). Prepare according to the directions for sesame salt. On the average, about one-and-a-half teaspoons of the above powders may be eaten daily by adults.
- *Umeboshi plum:* Plums which have been dried and pickled for over one year with sea salt are called *ume* (plum) *boshi* (dry) in Japanese. On the average, adults may eat two to three plums per week. Umeboshi stimulates the appetite and digestion and aids in maintaining an alkaline blood quality. Older children may enjoy them on occasion.
- *Shio (salt) kombu:* Soak one cup of kombu until soft and cut into one-quarter-inch-square pieces. Add to a half-cup of water and a half-cup of tamari, bring to a boil and simmer until the liquid evaporates. Cool and put in a covered jar to keep several days. One to two pieces may be used by adults on occasion as needed.
- *Nori condiment:* Cut or tear sheets of nori into one-inch squares. In approximately one cup of water, simmer until the ingredients cook down to a thick paste. Add enough tamari soy sauce for a moderately salty flavor. Adults may eat a teaspoon of nori condiment together with a meal on occasion.
- *Tekka:* This condiment is made from minced burdock, lotus root, carrot, miso, sesame oil, and ginger. It can be made at home or bought ready-made. It is recommended that adults use it sparingly due to its strong contracting nature, while children normally do not require it.

- *Sauerkraut:* Traditional sauerkraut is made from cabbage and sea salt. A small volume may be eaten occasionally with a meal by adults and older children.

Other condiments for occasional use include:
- *Pickles:* Adults or older children may enjoy a small volume of pickles on a regular basis. In general, quicker and less salty pickles are preferable for children. Pickles are not necessary for children before the age of two. An occasional small volume of very mild tasting pickles may be introduced after this. Light, mild pickles are also better for older people. If they are in good health they can be served pickles made with tamari and ginger on occasion.
- *Vinegar:* A moderate amount of brown rice and umeboshi vinegar may be used from time to time. Other vinegars are best avoided. Vinegar is generally not recommended for babies.
- *Ginger:* A small volume of ginger may be used occasionally as a garnish for adults or older children, or as a flavoring in vegetable dishes, soups, pickled vegetables, and especially with fish and seafood. Ginger is generally too strong for babies and small children.

8. *Oil and Seasoning*

It is best to use only a moderate amount of high quality, cold pressed vegetable oil in cooking. It is generally advisable to limit the intake of sautéed vegetables and other dishes which contain oil to several times per week, and to use only a small amount of oil when preparing those dishes. Oil may be used occasionally in deep-frying grains, vegetables, fish, and seafood.

It is not necessary for babies to have oil. Oil cannot be digested properly without using salt to balance it. Do not include oil in your children's diet until salt is introduced, and then in small quantities only. It is important for older adults to take a little more oil than young people, but it must be well balanced with the proper amounts of seasoning.

Oils for regular use include: Sesame, dark sesame, and corn oil.

Naturally processed, unrefined sea salt is preferred over other varieties of seasoning. Miso and tamari soy sauce, both of which contain sea salt, may also be used. It is recommended that only naturally processed, non-chemicalized varieties be used, and even these are best used only moderately in daily cooking. These seasonings are best omitted when preparing food for babies and small children. Please refer to Chapter Three for recommendations for introducing them to children as they grow older.

Seasonings that can be used regularly by adults and older children include: Miso, tamari soy sauce, white sea salt, umeboshi plum or paste, umeboshi vinegar, and rice or other grain vinegars.

It is better to avoid chemicalized, sugared, or artificial seasonings.

9. *Foods to Reduce or Avoid in Temperate Climates*

Animal Products
Red meat (beef, lamb, pork)
Poultry
Wild game
Eggs

Dairy Foods
Cheese
Butter
Milk (buttermilk, skim milk)
Yogurt
Kefir
Ice cream
Cream
Sour cream
Whipped cream
Margarine

Fish
Red meat or blue skinned fish such as:
    Tuna (though raw meat tuna may be
        served occasionally with tamari and
        a garnish of grated daikon or mustard)
    Salmon
    Swordfish
    Bluefish

Processed Foods
Instant foods
Canned foods
Frozen foods
Refined (white) flour
Polished (white) rice
Foods processed with:
    Chemicals
    Additives
    Preservatives
    Stabilizers
    Emulsifiers
    Artificial coloring
    Sprayed, dyed foods

Sweeteners
Sugar (white, raw, brown,
    turbinado)
Honey
Molasses
Corn syrup
Saccharine and other artificial
    sweeteners
Fructose
Carob
Maple syrup
Chocolate

Stimulants
Spices (cayenne, cumin, etc.)
Herbs
Vinegar
Coffee
Alcohol
Commercially dyed teas
Stimulating aromatic teas
    (herb, mint, etc.)
Ginseng

Fats
Lard or shortening
Processed vegetable oils
Soy margarines

Nuts
Brazil
Cashew
Pistachio
Hazel

Tropical Fruits-Beverages
Artificial beverages
    (sodas, cola, etc.)
Tropical or subtropical fruits:
    Bananas   Figs
    Grapefruit   Prunes
    Mangoes   Coconut
    Oranges   Kiwi
    Papayas

Food for Harmony

When whole natural foods are properly introduced into a family's diet, and when meals are prepared in a calm and loving manner, relations between the members of the family begin changing. As physical and mental hardness and rigidity dissolve, family members will notice their expressions becoming gentler and milder, and their attitude more caring and loving. Eventually, individual sensitivity can increase to the point that members of the family are able to understand each other without having to use words.

In traditional cultures throughout the world, love and harmony were the goal of family relations. In Japan, for example, peace or harmony is expressed in the character *Wa* (和). *Wa* is an important factor in family relations and in the organization of society itself.

Revealed in the letter or character for this word is the understanding of the importance of food in creating thought, behavior, and social relations. The character for *Wa* is formed by drawings that represent a *cereal plant* (禾) and a *mouth* (口). This implies that eating whole grains makes us peaceful and our relationship with other people harmonious. The principle of *Wa* applies as much to world peace and global harmony as it does to peaceful families. The path to social harmony and world peace lies in reestablishing whole cereal grains as main foods.

Families who do not know the importance of food face the likelihood of disharmony and eventual decomposition due to sickness, accident, divorce, or separation. Family decomposition is part of the modern trend toward social disharmony and possible collapse. Humanity faces the genuine possibility of global extinction through nuclear war or biological and psychological degeneration. Strong and healthy families are essential in reconstructing humanity and in turning our course away from destruction. They are our best hope for the future. We can no longer ignore the importance of food in the health and well-being of the family and society. To do so is to risk the continuation of the natural human race.

Home Cooking

Good cooking is essential for the health and well-being of every family. Whoever cooks for their family is building not only a healthy and peaceful home, but a healthy and peaceful world. We encourage all members of the family to study and practice this all-important art. The joy of selecting, preparing, and serving balanced natural foods can be taught to every child. All members of the family can help in the kitchen.

The flavor of foods can be varied. Children need a more naturally sweet taste, such as that of properly cooked grains and vegetables. Adults and elders may have a variety of tastes, while sick persons tend to dislike strongly flavored dishes, including those with spicy or bitter flavors.

Parents will want to carefully watch what their children eat and what they are attracted to. This is a very important point to keep in mind. If we observe what children eat, and then see how they behave afterward, we can learn much about

how to cook for them. Notice whether they are happy, sad, crying, fighting, or peaceful, and then remember what it was that they ate to make them this way.

Each child has different needs and wants. If we are sensitive to these differences, we can avoid many problems or sicknessess. Make suggestions to children about what to eat if they are older and able to understand the importance of food. Point out how the foods they eat affect their behavior. Explain how certain foods cause problems and how other foods are good for their health. However, for children to develop properly, parents need to be flexible. Give them the time to think about these ideas, and to make their own connection between food and their body and emotions. Rather than imposing rules or using discipline to make them believe, let children experience and discover things for themselves. If parents do not clearly understand the relationship between food and health, their method of handling these matters may become rigid or conceptual.[4]

A mother needs to be sensitive and caring enough to prepare her children's favorite foods for them. If she has several children, she may have to cook several "favorite" foods.

[4] *The Meaning of Variety:* When parents come for advice I often tell them that they or their children need more variety in their diets. Some misunderstand and think they can now have such items as sweet potatoes, yams, maple syrup, lots of beans, or plenty of fish. "Variety" refers not just to a number of different grains, beans, soups, sea vegetables, pickles, condiments, or desserts, but also to a variety of cooking methods, seasonings, garnishes, and cutting techniques. Do not cook the same way all the time or always use the same ingredients in the same dishes. Continually change your cooking to make it new, interesting, and appealing.— *Aveline Kushi.*

A Healthy Family Life

Along with selecting and preparing the right foods, families can eat together as often as possible, at least once a day. The health and well-being of every family member are also enhanced by keeping a clean, orderly, and natural environment in the home. The way we orient our daily lives—from the type of activity we engage in to the materials we choose for clothing, toys, and home furnishings—has a strong influence on all family members. The recommendations presented below can help the whole family enjoy a more natural, healthy, and satisfying way of life.

1. Chewing is essential for good health. We recommend chewing each mouth-.ful until it becomes liquid, as many as fifty times or more. Teach children how to chew properly while they are young. As they grow older, remind them from time to time that chewing is good for them. Parents, be aware that your practice of good chewing, healthful eating, and other positive health habits serves as an ongoing example for your children.
2. Eat only when hungry. Children and older family members may eat whenever they want to and may enjoy natural wholesome snacks from time to time, but it is better to avoid habitual overeating.
3. Eat in an orderly manner. Encourage everyone in the family, including children, to treat food with love and care. Eat only when sitting and encourage children to be calm during meals and not to eat while standing, walking, running, playing or while involved in other activities such as watch-

ing television. Everyone may eat regularly two to three times per day, as much as they want, provided each meal includes the correct proportions of food and each mouthful is chewed thoroughly. Children may eat more frequently when necessary and may enjoy natural snacks from time to time, but again, try to discourage overeating. Habitual snacking can interfere with the eating of more regular and nutritionally complete meals.[5]

4. It is better to leave the table feeling satisfied but not full. To prevent wasting food, avoid overloading children's plates. Instead serve the approximate amount of food that they can finish. Additional servings can be given as

---

[5] *Developing Good Habits:* It is very important to teach children how to eat properly. And it is easier to teach correct eating habits when children are young. Undesirable habits formed in childhood are difficult for teenagers or adults to break. I remember when I was in college studying Zen. We could make no noise during meals. It was very strict, hard training. Of course, we can be more relaxed at home. It is better to keep the home atmosphere more relaxed and enjoyable, but simple table manners will benefit the entire family. This includes such points as keeping a straight but not rigid spine while eating, chewing well, and not eating with the fingers. It is naturally easier to catch and correct problems when children are young. If we wait until children become teenagers it is much more difficult and may result in arguments and disagreements. Giving thanks or appreciation before each meal, or praying to God or nature for your food is also recommended, as it is important to teach children gratitude. If these simple things— manners, thankfulness, and togetherness—are observed by your family, many problems can be solved or avoided.

Really try to have only the best quality food available for your family. This is the key to health. If the members of your family keep good health, very few problems will arise.— *Aveline Kushi.*

needed or requested. Adults are also advised to avoid leaving food on their plate.[6]

5. Drink comfortably but not excessively. Children may drink a slightly larger amount of liquid than adults, but excessive or habitual drinking is best discouraged. Do not be inflexible about this. If children are excessively thirsty, allow them to drink as desired. At the same time, parents should find and eliminate whatever it is that is causing the thirst.

6. For optimum health, it is best for adults to avoid eating for three hours before sleeping, as going to bed shortly after eating creates stagnation in the intestines, sluggish digestion, inefficient absorption, and accumulation of excess throughout the body. Children may eat a little bit closer to bedtime, but for optimum health, it is better for them to avoid eating just before sleeping, except of course for nursing infants.

7. Wash as needed, but avoid long hot baths or showers. It is better for children not to take very hot baths or remain in the tub or shower until their skin becomes wrinkled as this drains minerals from the body.

8. We recommend that everyone scrub and massage their entire body with a hot damp towel until the skin becomes red, every morning and/or night. At the very least, scrub the hands and feet, taking time to do each finger and toe. Scrubbing activates circulation and the flow of energy throughout the body. Parents can do this for their children and, when they become old enough, encourage them to do it themselves as a daily health habit. A hot towel rub makes one feel refreshed and renewed.

9. Encourage family members to wear only cotton clothing directly next to the skin, and especially cotton undergarments. Cotton allows the skin to breathe and exchange energy with the environment. It is better to avoid wearing synthetic, woolen, or silk clothing directly on the skin. Many shops and mail order houses sell high quality cotton baby and children's clothing and accessories. It is better for adults to avoid wearing excessive metallic jewelry or accessories on the fingers, wrists or neck, and to keep such ornaments simple, graceful and as natural as possible.

10. For the deepest and most restful sleep, adults can go to bed before midnight and get up early in the morning. It is best for children to also go to bed and get up at regular times as this establishes a more harmonious natural rhythm.

---

[6] *Children's Portions:* The way of feeding babies and small children is very important. Serve small portions instead of giving them too much food or too many dishes at once. When they have cleaned their plate and want more, then give them a small amount again. In this way children do not waste food, the table is never messy, and they learn to always finish what is on their plate without parents having to use discipline. Often mothers put too much food on children's plates. When children are eating, watch them and help or correct them if necessary. It is better not to habitually give between-meal snacks, if possible. When children are really hungry, serve them rice balls or other healthful snacks. Sometimes children crave fruit, and when this happens, try to keep their intake moderate. If we watch them carefully, we can really guide and manage our children's condition.—*Aveline Kushi.*

11. Encourage every member of the family to be as active as possible in daily life and to participate in home activities such as cooking, scrubbing floors, cleaning windows, and washing clothes. Children can participate in simple household chores such as cleaning, sweeping, cooking, doing dishes, raking leaves, shoveling snow, and taking out the trash. Systematic exercise programs such as yoga, Dō-In and sports are also healthy and enjoyable and are things that the entire family can do together. It is important to encourage children to develop physical strength, flexibility, and endurance so that they may enjoy a healthy and productive life. Children can also be invited to assist with cooking or to try cooking themselves from time to time, of course with proper supervision.

12. If their conditions permit, encourage everyone in the family to often go outdoors in simple clothing, and whenever possible, to walk barefoot on the beach, grass, or soil. It is important for children to play outside in the sunshine whenever possible, preferably once a day, regardless of the season. Frequent family outings to the beach, mountains, parks or other outdoor recreation areas are also recommended. Encourage children to have regular contact with nature as a means of developing a sense of wonder, marvel, and appreciation.

13. Keep the home clean and orderly. Pay particular attention to the areas where food is prepared and served. As much as possible, involve children in daily cleanup activities. Keep children's sleeping and play areas clean and orderly and encourage them to take responsibility for keeping these areas neat and clean.

14. Use natural materials in the home. Cotton sheets, *futon*s, towels, and pillowcases, incandescent lighting, natural wood furnishings, and cotton or wool carpets all contribute toward a softer and more natural home environment. Try to keep children's toys and playthings as natural as possible; for example, the energy of wooden toys is preferable to that of toys made from plastic or metal or to the energy of electronic devices.

15. It is advisable to use a gas or wood stove for home cooking rather than electric or microwave cooking devices.

16. Avoid or minimize the use of electric objects close to the body, including electric shavers, hair dryers, stereo headsets, blankets, heating pads, toothbrushes, toys, and others.

17. Keep large green plants in the home to freshen and enrich the air. Plants can also be placed in children's sleeping and play areas. Open windows daily to permit fresh air to circulate, even for a short time in the cold weather.

18. Use earthenware, cast iron, or stainless steel cookware in the kitchen, rather than aluminum or teflon coated pots.

19. If anyone in the family watches television, encourage them to do so at a distance and at an angle to the set in order to minimize exposure to radiation. Color television is best minimized or avoided for maximum health, as is watching television during mealtimes. It is better to encourage children to develop creativity and imagination through study, reading, art, music, sports,

daily chores, hobbies, or playing outside rather than allowing their natural capacities to wither as the result of an over-dependence upon television, video games or other forms of pre-packaged entertainment.[7]

According to recent surveys, the average American household watches television for more than seven hours each day. In a survey conducted by the American Academy of Pediatrics, children between the ages two to twelve were found to spend an average of 25 hours a week in front of the television. Many were found to spend more time watching television than in school. The Academy also found that television viewing promoted the eating of poor quality foods and obesity. Many of the commercials on television feature high fat and highly sugared foods. Children often eat while watching television and are much less physically active. The so-called "video-revolution" of the 1980s, in which cable television, VCRs, and video games have proliferated, has increased the potential for excessive viewing on the part of children and other members of the family.

Encourage children to participate in life through direct experience and not to content themselves with the role of a spectator. Encourage them to continually challenge themselves physically, intellectually, and creatively.

20. Avoid chemically produced cosmetics and body care products in the home. Use natural soaps for laundry and washing, and natural toothpaste, sea salt, *dentie*, or clay for tooth care.

Family Spirit

The members of a family share a similar origin: Webster's for example, defines the family as "descendants of one common ancestor." Brothers and sisters share the same parents, and parents in turn have their respective parents and ancestors. Children are the most recent links in an ancestral chain that stretches back for thousands of generations to the origins of humanity itself.

We exist because of our ancestors. We cannot deny them nor can we separate ourselves from them.

In most traditional societies, people were deeply aware of their relationship to

---

[7] *Family Entertainment:* Families do not sing together as they often did in the past. Children should sing at home and at school. When my children were small, we would often sing together, but since we did not know many English songs, we usually sang Japanese ones.

It is not a good idea to let children watch television for many hours at a time. Children should be encouraged not to watch programs that are violent or show wild, strange, or sexual behavior or that contain vulgar language. Such shows are best avoided, as they disturb a child's natural perception and can blind children to many things around them. Select only the most suitable movies, television shows, or music for them. Encourage children to play outside whenever possible and take them often to parks or outdoor play areas. Ask them to help clean house or be active in sports rather than watching television. If children are watching too much television, parents can spend more time with them. Ideally, the more natural environment of the countryside is best for children to live in, as it enables youngsters to observe nature and the changing of the seasons more clearly than they can in the city.—*Aveline Kushi.*

their ancestors. Love and respect for one's parents and ancestors was seen as being the same as love and respect for oneself. Love and respect for parents, elders, and ancestors was considered one of the most fundamental virtues.

America is young in comparison to the cultures of Europe and the Far East. When people immigrated here they often lost contact with their families back home, and an awareness of their ancestors was also diminished. Many people are not aware of their family histories for more than several generations, while people in other parts of the world frequently can trace their family histories back hundreds of years.

Our family has lived in a village in southern Japan for many centuries. There is a temple in the village that our ancestors have helped to maintain for nearly twelve hundred years. Within the temple grounds is a cemetery where, for several hundred years, our ancestors have been buried. Whenever we visit that place we feel deeply inspired and come away with gratitude toward our ancestors and a clearer sense of the continuity of existence.

One way to affirm continuity with our ancestors is to visit their graves from time to time in order to extend appreciation. Bring children along so that they can also develop a sense of family history. If your family's ancestors are not buried in one place, think about establishing a central location in the future so that this tradition can continue among future descendants.

What are the most important things to give to future generations? Some might answer money, property, titles, stocks, or a bank account. Actually, material things are relatively insignificant when compared to intangibles such as a dream of life and aspiration toward an endless future. One of the most valuable things to leave for future generations, aside from the knowledge of how to maintain their health, is the dream of establishing a healthy and peaceful world, together with love for all people. Money, titles, fame, and wealth come and go like tides in the ocean, but the dream of health and peace is imperishable.

A family record is also invaluable. It can include information such as parents' names, where and when they were born, and what they did during their lives. Information about uncles, aunts, grandparents, and other relatives and ancestors can also be included, together with a history of our own life and activities.

Parents whose families do not yet have a family record may want to begin one. Make a set for each child. Ask them to add information about their lives when they get older, and to make copies to give to each of their children. Grandchildren can continue to add information and eventually pass copies on to the next generation. A family record will come to have great meaning for our descendants. It can serve as a source of continuity for centuries to come.

After experiencing many ups and downs and successes and failures in life, we can write down our conclusions, perhaps summarizing them in ten or twenty key points. Our philosophy of life can be given to our children along with our family record. Advice and wisdom about spiritual matters and about life in general is actually far more important than a will in which our estate is divided among relatives.

These records were known in the Orient as *Ka-kun,* or "family teachings." Many traditional families accumulated wisdom from generation to generation in this form. In some cases, the family teachings contain practical recommendations for daily life such as "get up early in the morning" or "study for several hours everyday," while others deal with broader ethical, social or spiritual questions. When we compile our teachings, we should try to present a summary of our life experience so that our descendants may benefit from it.

As we have seen, educating ourselves and our children about proper food is very important. Respect and gratitude for ancestors complements a balanced, natural diet. If either of these aspects is missing, a family faces eventual collapse. Both are needed for the health and well-being of the family and society at large.

Today, people often marry without knowing much about their own or their partner's family spirit or history. Some marriages result from sensory or emotional attraction only. Most marriages are built on a shaky foundation. Small problems are often enough to destroy the relationship. The tendency today is for both partners to give up and say good-bye rather than trying to solve their difficulties. Before children are born, the effects of divorce or separation are not as serious or long lasting. However, once a couple has children, the effects are much more serious. Although they may not be able to express it, the children of divorced parents frequently feel deeply disappointed and resentful. They sometimes become depressed and distrustful of other people. The breakup of a family is a very unhappy experience for a child.

Parents naturally place their children at the center of their universe. Their health and well-being come first. Proper nourishment of children—through diet and spiritual awareness—is the most important issue that parents face. The well-being of children comes before other considerations. Parents continually pour love and energy into nourishing and guiding them properly, even if they have to change their job, place of living, lifestyle, or method of cooking for the benefit of their children.

Love and care for children are the strongest human instincts, even stronger than the instinct for self-preservation. They develop quite naturally when we eat a diet of grains and vegetables. Family and community solidarity occur quite naturally among whole grain and vegetable eaters, while the modern diet produces greater isolation. People who are isolated tend to see their world as separate and distinct from that of their children.

Separation is the hallmark of our modern age: separation between man and nature, husband and wife, parents and children, body and mind, and between neighbors on the same street and neighbors in other parts of the globe. If we are to continue on this planet in an age of nuclear weapons, separation, conflict and isolation must be transformed into unity, harmony, and cooperation. Family health is the key to world peace.

Establishing a planetary commonwealth of humanity—a kind of global extended family—offers a clear alternative to present destructive trends. It will come about when the members of the human family begin to eat according to universal principles and establish a similar quality of blood and a common dream of health and peace.

Chapter **2**
How Children Develop

The splendor of creation can be found in each flower, grain of sand, and individual child. The creative forces that form the largest galaxies, the most delicate flowers, and the tiniest atoms are revealed in a child's daily life.

Endless cycles of birth, growth, development, and maturity are at the root of all things, including human beings. Nowhere are these cycles more apparent than in children. Children change from day to day and moment to moment, transforming themselves before our eyes. Universal order is manifest in the life of every child.

A baby changes dramatically during the first two years. He or she learns to walk, to use arms, legs, hands, and fingers, to utter simple words, and to take food independently of the mother. Children develop a unique personality and a sense of self.

In this chapter, we trace the major landmarks of childhood development until puberty. We also present an overview of human development in general, especially in the realm of consciousness, and see how the changes that take place during childhood fit in with the overall pattern of human development.

By viewing the stages of child development from the macrobiotic perspective, we hope readers will be encouraged to see childhood, and by extension, all life, in a far larger context than is usually considered. Using the terms yin and yang to represent the basic opposite yet complementary tendencies in life, and the spirallic pattern to explain physical, emotional and mental growth, illustrates how human life reflects, and is in perfect harmony with, the vast order of the infinite universe.

We hope that the examples that follow will enable readers to begin seeing this order in every area of life. Then, when reference books are consulted for more detailed information on child development, readers will be able to understand growth as the expression of the cycles of "nature" in the largest sense of the word.

Developments Before Birth

The most dramatic physical developments actually take place before a child is born. If it were possible to gaze inside the womb, we would witness the growth of a single fertilized cell—too small to be seen with the naked eye—into a new human being with trillions of cells arranged according to a blueprint drawn up over billions of years of evolution.

During the nine months of pregnancy, a human baby passes through an enormous span of evolutionary history, beginning as single-celled life, continuing through water life, and ending like the first amphibians that ventured onto dry land. It took the enormous span of about 2.8 billion years for air-breathing animals to develop on earth, yet human beings accomplish the whole process in only 280 days.

The birth of a baby corresponds to the transition from life in the primordial ocean to life on the surface of the earth, a transition that occurred about 400 million years ago. During each day of pregnancy, the baby passes through the equivalent of roughly 10 million years of biological evolution. The physical, emotional, and spiritual nourishment received by the baby during pregnancy is therefore vitally important. *Tai-kyo*, the approach to prenatal care practiced in Japan and other traditional cultures, is based on the importance of a balanced natural diet, an orderly life, and calm and peaceful thoughts and emotions during pregnancy. (It is covered in detail in our other family health book, *Macrobiotic Pregnancy and Care of the Newborn*.) The baby's fundamental constitution, including the potential for health or sickness, wisdom or foolishness, broad- or narrow-mindedness, and success or failure in life is largely determined by the mother's diet and way of life during pregnancy.

Developments Following Birth

Although the speed becomes less rapid, a baby develops very actively following birth. The entire span of evolution, from the first single-celled life to the appearance of homo sapiens, took about 3.2 billion years to accomplish. Human beings repeat the whole process. At birth, the equivalent of seven-eighths of the process is complete; the remaining one-eighth—the approximately 400 million years during which life evolved on land—is replicated during the first two years of infancy. This epoch of evolution encompasses the stages of amphibians, reptiles, mammals, monkeys, apes and ultimately, man. A newborn passes, step by step, through the equivalent of these stages.

Changes in posture and movement reflect these stages in evolutionary development. The earliest attempts to turn over and lift the head and crawl, correspond to the wriggling movements and belly-down posture of amphibians and reptiles. A baby then starts to crawl in a fashion not unlike that of four-legged mammals, and to half-stand like monkeys and other primates. Finally, an infant stands erect without assistance and takes his or her first tentative steps. The baby is now ready to begin developing in a manner that is uniquely human.

The span between birth and standing corresponds to about 400 million years of evolution, and a baby condenses these developments into approximately 12 to 18 months. That means that the baby passes through the equivalent of about 33 million years of evolutionary development every month, one million years each day, 40,000 years every hour, and more than 600 years every minute. Because development occurs so rapidly during this time, the quality of nourishment that the baby receives is vitally important, as is the type of environment at home and the love and care provided by the parents.

The Influence of Food

Food begins to influence the baby even before conception. It does this by affecting the quality of the parents' reproductive cells and the genetic factors that they contain. The foods eaten by the mother create the quality of her blood, cells and tissues, and influence the development and maturation of her ova, or egg cells, while the quality of the father's sperm is largely due to the foods that he eats. During pregnancy, the placenta provides nourishment for the baby directly from the mother's blood, the quality and composition of which is determined by the foods that she eats. The nutrients in mother's blood are very condensed. (In general, foods that originate from animal sources are classified as having a more yang or constrictive quality, while vegetable products are classified as more yin or expansive.) After being nourished by this type of food for nine months, babies have a more yang quality at birth. They are tiny, wrinkled, and their arms and legs are curled into tightly wound spirals.

The more yang head normally assumes a downward position during delivery and at birth is larger in relation to the rest of the body than it is later in life. During the first trimester, the head forms about one-half of the entire body. It averages about one-fourth of the body size at birth. In adults, the head averages about one-eighth of the total body size. The comparative size of the brain also decreases as a child grows. At birth, the brain makes up about 10 percent of the body weight, while in adults it makes up only about 2 percent.

After birth, nourishment is naturally provided in the form of *colostrum*, a clear liquid secreted by the breasts for several days before milk comes in. It contains antibodies and other factors that convey natural immunity to the baby. Colostrum is thinner, clearer, and more yin than mother's blood, while mother's milk, which is sweet and rich, has a more yin quality than colostrum.

By distilling its nourishment directly from mother's blood, the single fertilized cell is able to develop with incredible speed, so that nearly 3 billion years of evolution are condensed into nine months. Mother's milk, a slightly less concentrated form of mother's blood that is secreted externally, also causes the baby to develop rapidly, although at a slower pace than previously.

During the time that an infant nurses, more of the yin components of breast milk—especially certain carbohydrates, fats, and proteins—are attracted to the more yang head. More of the yang components are attracted toward the legs and lower body, both of which are originally more yin than the head. The head, originally in a downward position at birth, gradually assumes a more yin upward position, while the arms, legs, and lower body become more active and well developed and able to support the head and upper body. As these developments occur, the baby gradually changes from a more yang horizontal posture (lying down) to a more yin vertical one (standing).

The more yin quality of breast milk causes the baby to change to a lighter color, while fat cells are deposited below the surface of the skin, smoothing out wrinkles and rounding the contours of the bones and muscles. The baby begins to take on a softer and more well rounded appearance. The arms and legs are held tightly coiled and close to the body at birth. They gradually relax and unwind as the baby becomes more yin.

The type of food that a baby receives following birth provides the foundation for these developments. When a mother eats a well balanced diet and breast-feeds her baby, her milk provides the nourishment needed by the baby to accomplish the remaining course of evolution and enjoy a healthy life as a human being.

How Consciousness Grows

All levels of consciousness function through the intuition which everyone possesses. Intuition can easily be suppressed by an education that is narrow or one-sided, or dulled through improper diet; however, the potential for developing all the levels of consciousness exists in every child. Children intuitively know the purpose of life, which is to play happily on this earth and freely realize their dreams together with many other people. Because their physical conditions are normally flexible and unspoiled, children do not feel isolated from the larger currents of life. They have an intuitive faith in life and a seemingly limitless capacity for imagination, freedom, creativity, and adventure. Children are not constrained by time. They instinctively sense that the future is unlimited, and are capable of enjoying every moment as if it were an eternity.

Children can display an inner happiness and contentment that is based on their

Figure 4   The Spiral of Consciousness

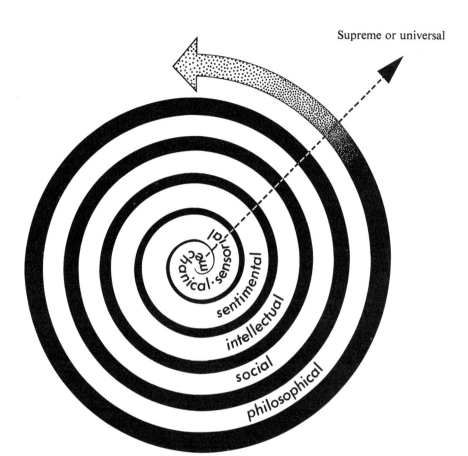

faith in the order of life and nature and their ability to freely realize their dreams and become whatever they want to in life. Children often say, "When I grow up, I want to become a fireman, a doctor, etc.," with full confidence that whatever it is they want to do is possible and achievable. At the same time, when they play, children freely assume a variety of roles which adults would find contradictory— one minute they are cops, the next, robbers; they can shift from being a hero to a villain and back again without any sense of contradiction.

Many spiritual teachers pointed to these and similar attributes as being qualities of a state in which intuition is allowed to function with little artificial interference. In the *Gospel According to Thomas*, for example, Jesus says, "Let him who seeks, not cease seeking until he finds, and when he finds, he will be troubled, and when he has been troubled, he will marvel and he will reign over the All." Children naturally possess this sense of marvel: They are able to find wonder and delight in a flower, a dog, in themselves, in an old toy, or in the ocean, sky, mountains, fields, and trees.

In another passage of the *Gospel According to Thomas*, we read, "Jesus saw little children who were being suckled. He said to his disciples: 'These children who are being suckled are like those who enter the Kingdom.' They said to him: 'Shall we then, being children, enter the Kingdom?' Jesus said to them: 'When you make the two one, and when you make the inner as the outer and the above as the below, and when you make the male and female into a single one, so that the male will not be male and the female not be female, when you make eyes in the place of an eye, and a hand in the place of a hand, and a foot in the place of a foot, an image in the place of an image, then shall you enter the Kingdom.' " As we have seen, children have the flexibility to unite seemingly opposite qualities and to freely shift from one role to the next in the course of their play. These are the attributes that Jesus describes.

The level of a child's consciousness continues to expand in scope throughout his or her life. Sensory perception and physical, or mechanical coordination are continually refined as a child learns to use tools and develops other motor skills. Meanwhile, emotional responses are refined and expanded during childhood, as the capacity grows to love and be loved, to give and receive, and to develop respect for oneself and for others. At puberty, and through adolescence, children begin to broaden their range of emotions as attraction for the opposite sex awakens and develops. Emotional sensitivity continually deepens and widens throughout life.

Intellectual abilities develop rapidly during childhood. Children learn how to figure things out, solve problems, to read and write, and to develop and expand their language abilities. They begin to see how things are connected and develop an awareness of where things come from and how situations develop. They also become aware that certain actions will produce certain results while opposite actions will produce opposite results. The ability to form concepts, make informed choices, and to arrange one's ideas in an orderly sequence develops rapidly during childhood and adolescence. Although the basic foundation of intellectual consciousness is laid during these early formative years, new knowledge, information and insights are added throughout life. Our conception of the world continually broadens as new dimensions of understanding are added.

As children grow, they become increasingly aware of the world outside the family. They associate with friends and classmates, and start to relate to the larger society both as individuals and as members of various groups. Their basic sense of how to relate to other people comes largely from their family experiences in early life, even as the scope of social awareness grows to include a concern for humanity and the world as a whole.

Social consciousness deals with our relationship to other people and ultimately, to how we relate to the planetary family of humanity. Philosophical, or spiritual consciousness encompasses these relationships, and extends beyond them into the realm of our relationship to God, or the universe. The seeds of philosophical under-standing can appear during childhood. Children sometimes ask, "Mommy, where did I come from?" "What is God?" "Why do I have five fingers, one nose, one mouth, and two ears?" and "Where did grandfather go after he died?" Like everyone else, children do wonder about the most basic questions of existence. Parents can provide them with proper guidance to pursue their lifelong quest for solutions.

The potential for developing through all of the levels of consciousness, including supreme or universal consciousness, begins during childhood. Whether or not consiousness matures fully during life depends, to a large degree, on the quality of early care that children receive. (Please refer to *The Book of Macrobiotics: The Universal Way of Health, Happiness, and Peace* by the author for further explana-tion of the seven levels of consciousness.)

Diet and the Development of Consciousness

How children are nourished during early life is one of the most important aspects of child care. The full development of consciousness depends on a properly nour-ished and healthy body, including the proper functioning of the brain and nervous system.

The decision of whether to feed an infant breast milk or a substitute will have a fundamental influence on the entire life of the child. The subject of infant nutri-tion is crucial not only to the child's physical, mental and spiritual health, but also to the quality of the relationships that develop within the family.

The following section explains in detail the effects of mother's milk and alter-native forms of nourishment on the developing infant. We hope readers will con-sider this matter seriously, and investigate further if there are any questions. There are many excellent books available.

At least 80 percent of human brain development occurs during pregnancy and the first three years of life. Therefore, how a mother eats throughout pregnancy—especially during the final trimester when brain development is rapid—is vitally important, as is the quality of food eaten by the child during the first three years. In studies conducted on animals, dietary deficiencies have been shown to negatively affect the brain, producing such physical damage as reductions in the size of the brain and in the number of cells that it contains, and disruption in the balance of brain enzymes. Disturbances such as these can impede normal brain function and the proper maturation of consciousness. Research has also linked inadequate diets during infancy and early childhood to developmental problems such as impaired physical control, clumsiness, overexcitability, and a lowered threshold to environmental stimuli. Current evidence points to decreased intellectual capacity among inadequately nourished children, affecting their physical and mental coordination, language skills, and capacities for social interaction.

When a mother eats a well-balanced diet, however, her milk contains the proper balance of nutrients that are essential for the normal development of the brain and nervous system. The composition of mother's milk changes as the baby continues nursing so as to meet the rapidly changing needs of the baby, including the rapid growth and development of the brain.

No other form of nourishment meets these needs as efficiently. In fact, recent studies show that other forms of nourishment—such as cow's milk formula—may impede normal brain functioning and development. An article published by the La Leche League in 1976, entitled *"Biological Specificity of Milk,"* by W. B. Whitestone, contained a report on studies that have shown that breast-fed children developed better reading and spelling skills than their counterparts who were fed cow's milk formulas.

Human infants are unique in the animal kingdom in that so much of their early nourishment is used for the development and growth of the brain. The human brain is about 23 percent of its adult size at birth, while the brain of a calf is nearly 100 percent developed at birth. A calf gains up to 75 percent of its adult weight during the first six weeks, and needs plenty of protein and minerals for the growth of muscle and bones. Human infants, on the average, gain less than a pound per week during the first six weeks. Their need for protein and minerals is much less than that of a calf, but their need for carbohydrates—which are used in the formation of healthy nerve and brain cells—is much greater. Cow's milk is naturally better suited to the rapid growth and development of the calf's massive bone and body structure; it contains up to three times as much protein and four times as much calcium as human milk. However, cow's milk is not the ideal food for brain development. Human milk, with up to twice as many carbohydrates, is far better suited to the growth and development of the human brain and nervous system.

Since cow's milk is lacking in carbohydrates, some type of sugar is generally added to cow's milk formulas to provide enough calories, usually in the form of cane sugar, brown sugar, or corn syrup. However, simple sugars such as these destroy B-complex vitamins, including thiamine, or vitamin B_1, which is naturally present in the outer layers of brown rice and other whole cereal grains. Thiamine and other B-vitamins are essential for healthy development and functioning of the nervous system, including the capacity for learning. If enough of these vitamins are destroyed, a child can develop difficulty in digesting carbohydrates and an excess of pyruvic acid can accumulate in the blood, resulting in an oxygen deficiency. Lack of oxygen can easily impair the functioning and development of the brain, which depends on oxygen and glucose for energy.

The intake of refined and other simple sugars disrupts the body's normal levels of blood glucose. The more sugar one consumes, the lower the blood sugar level tends to be. The brain uses about 50 percent of the glucose in the blood, and when the blood glucose level is disrupted, the functioning of the brain is affected. Sugar also contributes to a depletion of the body's mineral reserves, some of which, including zinc, iron, and magnesium, are essential in glucose metabolism. Depletion of minerals contributes to reduction in the chemical energy needed by the brain. Whenever the energy available to the brain is reduced, the area that receives priority is the *limbic system*, the part of the brain that controls the automatic processes necessary to maintain life. The brain centers that control the higher levels of consciousness—including intellectual capacities and social adjustment—are the first to be denied sufficient energy.

The development and functioning of the brain and nervous system are closely related to the condition of the intestines and digestive tract, through which all nutrients are absorbed. The intake of cow's milk formulas disrupts the normal functioning of the digestive tract and is associated with ulcerative colitis, diarrheal infections, colic, and other digestive disturbances. Digestive upsets frequently produce behavioral disturbances. Problems such as periodic irritable crying, crankiness, crying during bowel movements, and in some cases, convulsions, have been noted in children suffering digestive reactions to cow's milk formulas.

Breast milk promotes a healthy acid medium in the intestines that encourages the development of beneficial bacteria, some of which synthesize B-complex vitamins. Cow's milk furthers the development of an alkaline medium in which harmful, putrefactive bacteria more easily flourish. It also lacks the compounds found in breast milk that make the intestinal tract resistant to harmful bacteria. Harmful bacteria interfere with the activities of the beneficial bacteria, including the synthesis of the B-complex vitamins necessary for normal brain functioning.

The structure of the baby's digestive tract suggests that whole cereal grains and other vegetable quality products are the ideal baby foods once solids are introduced. Unlike carnivores who have a short digestive tract, the human digestive system is long and convoluted. It is better suited to the digestion of whole grains and other plant fibers that do not rapidly decompose and produce toxic bacteria as animal proteins do. The putrefaction of animal proteins in the digestive system also destroys beneficial bacteria, including those that synthesize the B-vitamins that are necessary for the proper functioning and development of the brain.

The structure of the teeth and digestive system suggest that homo sapiens evolved on a mixed diet consisting largely of whole cereal grains, beans, seeds, fresh local vegetables and other vegetable quality foods, with animal products comprising a minority of average consumption. Animal quality food—mother's blood—was the only source of nourishment during the period of life in the womb. More yin quality animal food—mother's milk—is the most natural source during the period of nursing. Once the baby stands and teeth come in, the milk-drinking stage comes to an end. From then on, it is preferable for nourishment to come primarily from cooked vegetable quality foods.

The more yang quality of animal food eaten in the womb promotes the development of mechanical and rudimentary sensory consciousness. Mother's milk, a more yin form of animal food, promotes refinement of the baby's mechanical and sensory abilities and causes emotional consciousness to awaken and grow.

The development and refinement of consciousness beyond the milk-drinking stage depends on the introduction of properly prepared vegetable quality foods. If some animal foods are eaten, it is recommended that they comprise a minority of the child's intake. The consumption of a large volume of animal food tends to limit the development of consciousness to the sensory and mechanical levels. The higher and more refined stages depend more upon the intake of vegetable quality foods. The intake of milk or other dairy products beyond the normal milk-drinking period often limits the development of consciousness to the emotional or sentimental levels. The remaining levels of consciousness may fail to develop properly as a result.

Aside from having a fundamental influence on the development of consciousness, childhood diet is a primary factor in future health and well-being. Two health problems that are medically linked with a poor diet—obesity and heart diesease—begin with eating habits acquired during infancy and childhood. Dr. Anthony Gotto, president of the American Heart Association, stated recently: "The important thing is to get kids eating the right foods as early as possible. If they develop good eating habits when they are young, they are more likely to eat healthily when they are older."*

A naturally balanced diet—a diet that lowers or eliminates the risk of obesity, heart disease, cancer, and a host of physically and mentally debilitating disorders—is a fundamental aspect of macrobiotic child care. Starting children on the road to lifelong health and well-being is one of the most essential tasks of parenthood. Ideally, proper diet should begin even before birth in the way a mother and father eat prior to and during pregnancy. When parents eat a naturally balanced diet, they provide their children with the foundation for future health and the development of the fullest potential of consciousness. With good health and clear judgment, children will be well equipped to realize their dreams and to play happily on this earth throughout their lives.

How Babies Develop

In the period following birth, a baby learns how to coordinate basic mechanical and sensory functions and to use the body in new ways. These developments can be classified into two major types: more yang *gross motor developments*, involving the movement and control of the large muscles of the body, and more yin *fine motor development*, which includes more delicate muscle control and especially the coordination between eye and hand.

As the baby's senses develop and become more refined, mechanical abilities gradually come under sensory control. Earlier, non-conscious responses to sensory stimulation such as the various newborn reflexes, are referred to as *sensorimotor behavior*, while actions that are controlled consciously are referred to as *psychomotor behavior*.

---

* According to the American Health Foundation, 20 to 30 percent of American children between the ages of 5 and 18 have above average cholesterol levels resulting from a diet high in fats. Children with high cholesterol and blood fat levels tend to maintain higher levels throughout life and have a greater risk of heart disease. In March, 1984, the American Heart Association and the American Health Foundation called on parents to start their children on more healthful, low fat diets as early as possible as a means of preventing heart disease and other serious illnesses.

The senses develop from those dealing with the more yang, immediate environment to those dealing with vibrations coming from greater distances. The more immediate senses—touch, taste and smell—mature more rapidly than do hearing and sight—the senses that deal with more yin forms of vibration.

In the past, it was believed that a newborn's behavior was entirely reflexive and mechanical. It was felt that the senses took time to develop. However, researchers

have recently found that newborns have the capability to see, hear, smell, and respond to touch. Infants only hours old seem to have the ability to focus on objects that are placed in front of them. However, whether or not a newborn sees or hears in the same manner as an adult or an older child is still an open scientific question.

Infants can see and hear, but in a manner that is qualitatively different than the way adults or older children do. Being very yang, infants are better able to sense general vibrations, rather than isolating specific concrete physical objects or sounds. When a newborn looks at his mother's face, for example, he is "seeing" her vibrational quality and general physical characteristics and does not focus on her specific features. As the baby becomes more yin—larger and more expanded— the ability to sharply focus on more yang specific objects and sounds develops. It is therefore better not to force a newborn to focus on specific objects or sounds but let these abilities unfold naturally as the baby grows.

Learning to Walk

Newborns begin moving their arms and legs while in the womb and continue to do so after birth. A newborn's posture and movements reflect a more yang condition resulting from the intake of condensed animal food in the womb. Newborns move their arms and legs in a stiff and jerky manner, while keeping them more tightly curled and close to the body. The intake of mother's milk and other more yin forms of nourishment causes their movements and posture to become more graceful and relaxed as time passes.

The intake of a more yin quality of food also gradually causes the head to become more yin and gravitate toward an upward position. A baby begins lifting the head while lying on the stomach. The neck muscles gradually become strong enough to support the head in an upright position. When newborns are first held upright, the head has a tendency to fall forward and then move backward. Because the head tends to flip-flop, anyone who holds the baby must be careful to support the head properly. A baby gradually gains the ability to hold the head steady, although it still tilts slightly forward. Ultimately, the baby is able to hold the head steadily in a completely upright position and turn it to the left and right.

Babies use the ability to control the head to graduate to the next level of large muscle control: learning to roll over. They first roll over from front to back by

using the weight of the head to pull the body over. Then comes rolling over from back to front. When a baby can roll over, parents need to be aware that he or she can roll off of a bed, table, or sofa and must watch the baby carefully.

From the third to the sixth month, a baby gains the ability to sit when placed in an upright position without being supported. During the next three months, a baby learns to sit up without help. The more vertical posture of sitting increases a baby's range of perception and opens the possibility of new dimensions of consciousness. The rapidly developing brain can now receive electromagnetic energy directly from the heavens via the spiral on top of the head.

Crawling represents the next major step in the baby's development. The age at

Figure 5   Changes in Posture from △ (Horizontal) to ▽ (Vertical)

which babies start to crawl varies widely, usually occurring between the sixth and twelfth months. However, not all babies crawl; some go directly from sitting to standing.

Standing is one of the most recent developments in biological evolution. It usually occurs between the ninth and twelfth months, though some babies stand earlier. Standing opens possibilities for the growth and expansion of consciousness into uniquely human dimensions. Walking gives the baby independence and freedom of motion that increase the opportunities for learning and growth. Once a baby learns to stand, the next step is walking, and this normally occurs between the tenth and sixteenth months, although earlier and later walking are not uncommon.

When a baby begins to crawl and walk, he or she explores the world with a seemingly limitless curiosity. Parents often need to adjust their living arrangements to meet the baby's newfound abilities, for example by preventing the baby from getting into things that could be harmful, by keeping the baby away from stairs and open windows, and by continually monitoring the baby both inside the home and outside during waking hours.

Soon, a baby learns to stoop, pick things up, and carry them. Around the middle of the second year, babies learn how to climb stairs one step at a time with assistance and how to descend in the same manner. It takes a while longer for children to manage stairs by themselves. Running is the next skill to be developed, usually around eighteen months to two years. It is during this time that babies begin actively climbing up stairs and onto furniture by themselves, and need careful watching by the parents to avoid accidents.

Eye-Hand Coordination

While a baby is learning to walk, he or she also develops a variety of movements that require coordination between the eyes and hands. As babies gradually focus on objects, they begin to follow them from one side to the other and up and down. Babies also hold their hands in front of their faces, and enjoy looking at them, and eventually move their hands to their mouths whenever they want.

The automatic grasp reflex gradually diminishes and the baby learns how to reach out and consciously grasp things that it sees. Being very yang, babies usually pull things toward themselves and put them into their mouths. This normally occurs between three and six months, although it may occur sooner. By the sixth month, most babies have achieved enough coordination to be able to pass objects from hand to hand and to rake small things in with their fingers. They also develop the ability to bang objects that they are holding, and to grab things with both hands.

An important milestone is reached when a baby learns to grasp things by managing the complementary/antagonistic relationship between the thumb and index finger. Soon the baby develops the ability to pick up small objects, and then progresses from the simple grasping or moving of objects to the use of objects—such as a spoon or a cup—to accomplish a task. Early in the second year, children learn how to hold a cup with two hands and use a spoon, although they frequently spill food. They also learn how to let go of and drop things and eventually to throw objects—such as cups, bowls or toys—across short distances. Children often enjoy this as a game.

During the second year, a baby learns to place blocks on top of each other, to

drink from a cup, and to use a spoon. Soon the child will learn to use a variety of objects such as crayons and pencils. Before the end of the second year, the baby may enjoy playing with simple toys, and by the age of two, is usually able to open doors and to make simple marks on a piece of paper with a crayon or pencil.

Emotional Development

Interaction with the mother lies at the root of emotional development and is most complete when the baby is fed naturally at the breast. Feeding a baby artificially can interfere with emotional development by depriving the baby of immediate natural contact and stimulation. A baby naturally enjoys the stimulation provided by the breast and begins to recognize and enjoy the sound of the mother's voice and her overall quality. As a baby begins to focus on more concrete objects, he or she starts to recognize the details of the mother's face. Gradually, a baby recognizes the father, other members of the family, and other close people, and distinguishes familiar from unfamiliar people.

The period of nursing represents a transition from a condition of total biological dependence to a condition of greater independence. In the womb, mother and baby were one. At birth, a baby physically separates from the mother, periodically reconnecting to breast-feed, and begins interacting directly with the surrounding environment, eventually including other people. During the first year, a baby gradually adjusts to being physically separate from the mother and to the new environment. However, babies use their connection with the mother as the base from which they explore their new surroundings. As they assume an increasingly vertical posture, the capacity for remembering the past and anticipating the future starts to develop. Soon, a baby internalizes familiar people and places. Babies often cry when their mothers leave them alone or when they are placed in an unknown setting without any familiar people around. Babies also begin to anticipate the future, for example, by knowing that the mother, father, or other familiar people will return after separation or that crying will bring food or comforting from the mother.

The emotional climate of the family, and especially the mother's thoughts and emotions, produce deep and lasting effects on a baby's developing character. More positive, happy, and peaceful thoughts and emotions have more positive effects on the baby, while unhappy, disturbed, frightful, or depressed thoughts produce negative effects. The influence of thoughts and emotions on a baby's development is especially profound during pregnancy and during the period of nursing. If a mother, father and other members of the family are happy, positive, peaceful and emotionally well-balanced, a baby will tend to develop similar characteristics. On the other hand, parents who are negative, argumentative, or emotionally tense or restless often convey a similar emotional makeup to their children, especially when the children are given an unbalanced diet.

Teething

The twenty baby teeth normally come in during the first two and one-half years, although there is considerable variation in the age which the teeth appear. The teeth emerge as the baby changes from a horizontal to a vertical posture and indicate that the process of land evolution has been accomplished. When teeth appear, a baby can begin to eat whole cereal grains, local vegetables, beans, and other whole natural foods without first having them processed in the body of the mother. The coming in of teeth indicates that a baby's digestive tract is now ready to begin processing foods taken from the vegetable kingdom.

The first teeth usually come in around the age of six months, although they may appear as early as three months. The two lower front incisors are normally the first to come in, followed by four upper incisors several months later. At a year old, the two lower lateral incisors usually come in, as do the first four molars. The canine teeth then appear, usually at sixteen to eighteen months, followed normally by the remaining four molars between the twentieth and twenty-fourth months.

Some children experience discomfort as the teeth come in, including inflammation, swelling, and pain in the gums. Some experience discomfort during the entire period that teeth are constantly coming in. Fever and diarrhea sometimes accompany teething and may come on for up to four months before a tooth actually appears.

Problems with teething are the result of imbalances in the way of eating, either in the foods eaten by the nursing mother or in the foods given to the baby. More yin foods such as sugar, soft drinks, tropical fruits, highly acidic vegetables, spices, refined flour products, honey, and too much oil can interfere with the smooth development of the teeth and produce tooth malformation. They can also cause inflammation and discomfort with teething, as excessive factors in the bloodstream tend to gather around the emerging tooth so as to be discharged from the body. Cow's or goat's milk can also weaken the teeth and produce discomfort, as can too much salt or too many animal products in the diet of the nursing mother. Animal foods and salt can cause the developing jaw to contract and reduce the amount of space needed for the teeth to come in properly. Breast-feeding beyond the normal length of time can also have a harmful effect on the development of teeth.

Bowel and Bladder Control

Awareness of and control over bowel functions proceeds together with developments in the mouth, which is at the opposite end of the digestive tract. Newborns possess well-developed sucking and swallowing reflexes that allow them to eat and drink without thought or conscious effort. Similarly, bowel movements and urination occur without conscious participation. As babies become consciously aware of eating, they start to become aware of the sensations associated with elimination. From the twelfth to the eighteenth month, babies become increasingly conscious of bowel movements, and this corresponds to the appearance of the first molars and the ability to begin chewing foods. During the second half of the second year, at approximately the time when the remaining baby teeth come in, children become ready to learn to control bowel movements.

Voluntary control of the sphincter muscles normally becomes possible between the ages of twelve and eighteen months, although many children take longer learning to control their bowel movements. A baby begins to gain voluntary control over bowel movements and urination as liquid and solid nourishment become more distinct. Initially, liquids and solids are combined in one food— mother's milk. As a baby takes less mother's milk and more semi-solid foods, the distinction between solids and water becomes more pronounced. Semi-solid or solid foods create a more solid bowel movement, and the exercise of chewing stimulates the muscles of the entire digestive tract and helps make it possible to consciously contract the sphincter muscles. More yang, solid wastes are easier to hold onto and release in a controlled manner than are more yin, liquid wastes, and as bowel movements become more solid, they tend to occur less often and with more regularity.

Bowel control tends to occur anywhere from one to one-and-a-half years before a child gains control over urination, although in some cases they occur simultaneously. The age at which control over urination is achieved usually ranges from eighteen months to three years. Control over urination during sleep is usually the last step in gaining control over elimination. Night control is usually established after daytime control, although both may occur at the same time.

Learning to Talk

Babies begin talking in a very natural way, by making their own sounds and coming out with their own words. If they were not taught a language, they would probably invent their own, naming objects in the way that Adam did. By allowing babies to speak frequently in their own way, parents foster their creative abilities, as they will fashion sound according to their original perception of the world.

Parents need not teach any definite words to babies until they are about three or four months old. Then gradually introduce adult words, repeating them very slowly. Adults speak more rapidly than infants because adults' brain waves are shorter than children's. Therefore, when talking to children, speak more slowly than normal; then children can understand easily and will learn words more quickly. If we speak too rapidly, they have a more difficult time understanding. The same principle can be applied whenever children are read stories. If we read a story slowly, after one or two times children will understand and even memorize it very easily.

The language of babies is a highly symbolic one. A baby condenses many meanings into one word. Children have a full range of concepts but cannot formulate them in precise detail. The scope of babies' concepts is actually as broad as adults', but their concepts are not expressed in such analytical detail. The adult mentality gives clarity and precision to each part of that generalized understanding. An adult may use about ten thousand words to express concepts for which a child uses only about twenty. During the early period of mental development, if children are deluged with adult concepts, it will be more difficult for them to develop innate intuitive understanding. It is better to let children talk to themselves, to dogs, to flowers, to anything, in their own language. Then gradually more detailed adult expressions will emerge.

Babies begin making sounds as soon as they are born and begin to enjoy this new activity during their first three months. They become increasingly sociable and responsive during the second three months, smiling and giggling when someone talks to them. Children often begin imitating simple words after babbling in their own language for several months, usually during the nine-to-twelve month period. They often begin by saying "mama" or "dada," and recognizing the sound of their name. After their first birthday, babies often begin pointing at and naming things in their own intuitive language. As children approach the middle of their second year, they usually have about ten words in their vocabulary and begin stringing words together in simple phrases. By the age of two, children usually have more than three hundred words in their vocabularies and are able to make short sentences. They can understand simple sentences and enjoy listening to stories, looking at pictures in books, and making simple marks on a piece of paper with a crayon and pencil.

During the third year, a child's intellectual growth flourishes; his or her vocabulary normally expands to over a thousand words. The average two-and-a-half year old learns new words everyday and begins to speak in more complicated sentences.

At the same time that mental development is proceeding, children are also developing physically. Mental development follows physical development, and it is important for children to be active in both play and learning. It is better to minimize interference with a child's physical development. For example, if parents are overprotective or frequently pick up a child who is just learning to crawl or walk, development of independent abilities can be impaired. As we saw earlier, during the embryonic period a baby develops through the equivalent of about 10 million years of biological evolution each day. Developments in the womb equal roughly 2.8 billion years of water evolution. About a year and a half after birth, babies can stand up straight, eat their own food, walk and talk. This period of development corresponds to the remaining period of land evolution, totaling about 400 million years. That means that a baby passes through the equivalent of six to eight hundred years of biological evolution every minute during roughly the first one-and-a-half years. Interrupting a baby's natural crawling or walking interferes with the child's independent development during this period.

Crawling is very important to a baby, because it develops and strengthens the muscles and joints. Concomitant with this activity, children are also developing their brains and powers of consciousness. Only after babies have become proficient at one stage can they proceed normally to the next stage of physical and mental development. Therefore it is important for a child to be active and develop naturally at his or her own pace and not be interrupted or forced to develop according to an artificial schedule.

Speed of Development

No two children develop at the same rate. Although the general pattern of development is similar from baby to baby, the speed at which physical, emotional, and mental development takes place is unique for each child.

The large variation in the speed of development is due to differences in food. It is better if children are not given food that will cause them to mature too quickly. A diet containing dairy food, for example, will make children grow faster physically, but it is difficult for mental growth to keep up with the abnormally stimulated physical growth. A baby who grows teeth very early or who shows signs of maturing extremely early is suffering from an imbalanced diet, usually including a high percentage of animal protein. Protein is an essential factor for growth, but taken in excess it speeds up development beyond a healthy, natural rate. In temperate climates, it is better for animal food to comprise at most about one-eighth, or 15 percent, of the human diet. In most cases, babies do not need any animal food at all: They can grow very well obtaining all the protein they need from mother's milk and from vegetable-quality foods. Low fat, white-meat fish can be added to children's diets when they are older, if desired.

On the other hand, some children develop very slowly. Babies who are not walking by the time they are almost two could be suffering from excess salt in their diet or not enough fresh vegetables. Because of its constrictive, or more yang physiological influence, too much salt prevents a baby from expanding and growing normally. Fresh vegetables, on the other hand, are essential because of their expansive, or more yin physiological effects. However, it is recommended that babies be fed primarily lightly cooked rather than raw vegetables, since cooking makes the tough vegetable fibers more easily digestible. In the case of children who eat foods containing sugar, chemicals, or a large amount of fruit or fruit juice (such as daily orange juice), slow development could indicate another type of weakness: mental retardation caused by the harmful effects of these foods on the nervous system.

Early Childhood

The years from two to six are often referred to as *early childhood*. It is during these years that a child's spiral of growth widens considerably, with new physical, emotional, intellectual, and social developments taking place simultaneously. On the whole, children become increasingly conscious of themselves as individuals, and begin forming their own unique personality and sense of self. It is during this time that children start to become active outside the home and receive a great deal of influence from teachers, peers, and other people.

The major developments during early childhood are summarized below:

1. *Development of greater physical coordination.* Children use their vertical posture and increased mobility to develop a variety of skills. They learn to balance left and right, forward and backward, up and down, movement and rest, and tension and relaxation. They start to do things like climb stairs,

run, jump, sit in a chair, hop and skip, ride on a kiddy car, tricycle or bicycle, throw or catch a ball or beanbag, and walk in a straight line. Their movements gradually become more skillful and graceful and more like those of adults. Children learn to control the forces of heaven and earth within their bodies. Movements such as walking or running forward, jumping, throwing, standing up, and rolling or twirling toward the right require them to use more of the earth's expanding force. Walking backward, sitting down, catching a ball, or rolling or twirling toward the left require the use of heaven's downward force.

All movements occur because the various spirals of the human body are either contracted or rotated inward, or expanded or rotated outward. The arms, hands, and fingers can be curled either toward or away from the body, or rotated toward the right or left. The legs and feet also move with a similar pattern, as does the head, neck, spine, and torso. Running involves contracting each leg spiral toward the body and then thrusting it down and away from the body. It also involves coordination between the right side of the body which conducts more earth's force, and the left side of the body which conducts more heaven's force, as well as between the legs and lower body and arms and upper body. Walking and skipping, twisting the torso, throwing, catching, jumping, and other activities involve coordinating the body's various spiral structures with the forces of heaven and earth, or contraction and expansion. Children's bodily flexibility and conductivity to environmental energies causes them to explore the possibilities of movement with seemingly boundless energy, enthusiasm, and joy.

2. *Development of more refined sensory perception and motor control.* As mental and physical coordination become more refined, children gain the ability to

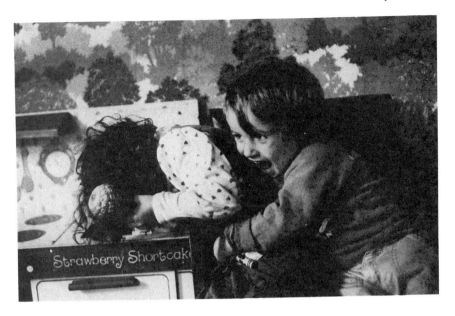

perform a variety of more delicate and controlled tasks. During the third year, they learn how to turn a doorknob, hold a crayon or pencil, unscrew the lids from jars, stack blocks on top of one another, and draw vertical lines. They also learn how to distinguish small objects at a distance and can often discriminate between small printed letters.

Children learn to control their fingers with greater skill during their fourth year, and can pick up small objects, handle scissors, and use a pencil in a more controlled way. During their fifth and sixth years, increasing fine muscle control enables them to do things like use scissors to cut on a straight line, draw a simple stick figure of the human body—sometimes with simple details such as eyes, a nose, a mouth, and hair—and copy simple block letters. The ability to hold a brush, pencil, or crayon continues to improve, so that as intellectual and language abilities develop, they become able to write letters, words, and numbers to make increasingly expressive and complicated drawings. Increasingly fine sensory abilities also make it possible for them to learn how to read.

3. *Development of a wider range of emotional responses.* Early childhood is a time of rapidly changing and seemingly contrasting emotions. Children alternate between feelings of independence and dependence; between self-importance and the sense of being a small part of a larger group; and between self-assertive or insistent behavior and easy-going and more flexible behavior. In general, however, children develop a greater sense of identity and individuality during these years, and become increasingly sensitive to the wishes of parents and other people. The important thing to remember is that children are flexible and that their behavior changes from one moment to the next. If children are eating well, their emotions are generally smooth and steady,

without the extreme tendencies produced by an excessive diet. Always remember that behavior and emotions are fluid and change in response to the child's environment and day to day diet.

One of the most noticeable aspects of childhood behavior is the alternation between more yang, *focal*, or concentrated activity, and more yin, *peripheral*, or diffuse activity. When children are going through a more focal stage, their energy is directed more inwardly. For example, they may not wish to go outside as much as usual, they may stick more closely to their mothers, and become less eager to get involved in new situations. During a more peripheral stage, children may have difficulty staying inside, sitting still, or focusing on one particular thing. They are often eager to explore new territory, meet new people, and try new things.

These and other complementary characteristics are influenced by the quality of food that a child receives and by the alternating rhythms of the environment. A diet based around more centrally balanced foods—whole cereal grains, beans, seasonal vegetables, and other supplementary items—promotes an even balance of both tendencies. Children who are nourished in a more balanced fashion tend to behave more evenly without becoming one-sided or extreme. They tend to be energetic yet peaceful; physically active and mentally bright; and strongly individualistic yet socially cooperative.

A diet based on extremes—for example, more yang items such as salt (especially in processed foods), and meat, eggs, poultry and other animal products; and more extremely yin items such as simple sugars, fruits, chemical additives, raw vegetables, and spices—promotes more excessive behavior.

Children who are fed such a diet often swing back and forth between extremes. They may become depressed or withdrawn with sudden outbursts of anger or crying; they may seem brashly self-confident and demanding and then suddenly become insecure and fearful; or they may become unpredictable, stubborn, or difficult to manage.

Behavior is also influenced by cyclic changes in the environment. Children are especially sensitive to these changes. Environmental energy continually changes from season to season, from full to new moon, from morning to evening, and from day to night. During the autumn and winter, environmental energy becomes more subtle and quiet. Behavior tends to become more focal and inward, and home activities like reading, listening to music, or playing with blocks or toys are more appealing at these times. During the spring and summer, nature erupts with expansive force. Outdoor play, physical activity, and more diffuse behavior naturally occur in these seasons.

As we approach the full moon, the energy in the atmosphere becomes more expansive. Children tend to be more active during this half of the lunar cycle. The new moon is a time of more quiet energy, and behavior tends to become more focal and inward as it approaches.

In the morning, children spring from their beds and actively begin their day. School children wash, dress, eat breakfast, and then leave home. Morning is a time of active, rising energy and more outgoing, energetic, and peripheral behavior. Conversely, downward energy predominates during the late afternoon, evening, and nighttime. Children are naturally more quiet, inward, and reflective during these times, eventually returning to their beds to sleep.

Understanding how behavior changes in response to environmental and dietary factors is invaluable in helping parents know why children act the way they do.

4. *Development of language and other intellectual abilities.* Children use their greater mechanical, sensory, and emotional powers to acquire language. The acquisition of language occurs as the result of the interplay between yang and yin, or input and outflow. Language skills develop through the alternating sequence of listening and speaking and reading and writing. As the range of input that a child receives widens—for example, to include words and letters as well as actual objects and feelings—so does the ability to respond with language. The acquisition of language occurs in the form of a spiral that becomes continually wider and more complex throughout life. The average rates at which new words are learned during early childhood are presented in the table below:

Table 5

Age	Average Number of Words
12 months	3
18 months	22
2 years	272
3 years	896
4 years	1,540
5 years	2,072
6 years	2,562

From *Early Childhood Years* by Theresa and Frank Caplan, Perigee, 1983.

As with all childhood development tables, including size and weight charts, these rates are estimated at best. A wide range of variation exists between one child and another.

Language itself has a variety of complementary functions, such as that existing between the more yang, self-directed function, and the more yin, outward-directed social function. When a child uses the self-directed function, he or she speaks as a form of self play, with little or no concern over whether someone else is listening. A child also uses language to communicate with others. At this time the social function of language becomes more important. As a child grows, self-directed speech becomes internalized in the form of thinking. Children shift flexibly back and forth between both aspects.

As children develop they learn to manage both the more yang sound vibrations of language and the more yin visual images of writing. When children learn to read, they do so by associating visual symbols, or letters, with both the corresponding sound vibration and with their image of the thing represented. It is better not to try to teach children to read before they show interest and are able to understand and speak to some extent, or in other words, until they have familiarized themselves with the vibrational aspect of spoken language.

Children learn about things by coming into direct contact with them. After seeing the brightness of the sun and experiencing the warmth of its rays, a child then develops an image and concept of the sun. The concept of water is established after children play in the bathtub or have a drink of cool clear water on a hot summer day. Ideas develop from the direct experience of things.

Children learn to think abstractly by playing with actual objects, for example, by touching them, lifting them, putting them in their mouths, and comparing them to other things. By playing with things they are learning to discern complementary, or yin and yang, tendencies such as large or small (size), more compact or more expanded (shape), brighter or darker (color), beginning, middle, and ending (sequence), hard or soft (texture), wet or dry (humidity), and hot or cold (temperature).

Yin and yang also provide the framework for understanding space and distance. Children begin to play with spatial relationships soon after birth, as they become aware of basic distinctions such as self and object, near and far, up and down, and left and right. Children initially use the more yang sense of touch to measure space, but as time passes, they start to rely on their more yin visual perceptions.

Studies on how children learn show a fairly uniform sequence of development. Learning abilities develop one after the other in stages. The same principle applies to the development of consciousness in general. One must fully develop through a particular level before the next one can be mastered. One cannot skip levels of consciousness nor can children be forced to learn certain concepts before they are ready.

5. *Development of social awareness.*   Social relations also develop in the form of an expanding spiral. Most of a child's social interaction takes place within the family. The dreams, values, and view of life of parents and other close family members are a primary influence in the development of a child's social outlook. Parents who are hardworking, humble, and who actively pursue a dream for the benefit of others convey these values to their children. A warm, cooperative, and loving atmosphere at home helps a child to become a warm and loving adult.

Children continually make balance between their vertical inner growth and their horizontal relation to their physical and social environments. Children use their developing motor, sensory, and language abilities to become increasingly active in social relationships. Around the age of two,

children tend to engage in what is known as *parallel play*. When placed with other toddlers, they tend to watch each other and engage in similar activities, but are playing more alongside rather than with their friends. By the age of three, however, they begin interacting more with others. They play together with their friends and begin to talk about what they are doing. They sometimes assume a variety of roles and begin to pretend. By the age of six, children usually engage in group play that involves a variety of more complex interrelationships.

6. *Development of food awareness.* Newborns eat in an instinctual and automatic manner. The sucking and swallowing reflexes are especially well developed at birth, and infants are strongly attracted to the sweetness of mother's milk. As the senses become further developed, babies begin to appreciate the taste and texture of foods and begin to recognize them by sight and smell. They derive pleasure from eating. When children are provided with a wide range of wholesome, natural foods, they learn to distinguish foods that are healthful and natural from those that are not. Children who do not eat meat or other fatty animal foods, for example, often find them repulsive and have no desire to eat them. As their range of social contact widens, children who eat a naturally balanced diet may find it difficult to understand why people eat foods that are unhealthful and, to them, unappealing. The preference for more balanced foods suggests that the instinct for maintaining health exists in children. When provided with the appropriate choices, children tend to select the foods that are the most wholesome and natural, although they may temporarily experiment with other foods as well.

7. *Development of natural awareness.* When provided with the proper environment, including a well-balanced diet, children develop a love and apprecia-

tion for nature. The alternating cycles of heaven and earth—such as day and night, waking and sleeping, movement and rest, and the progression of the seasons—provide the background for all learning and development. Experiencing these recurring patterns causes children to develop an intuitive faith in the order of the universe. This basic understanding lies at the root of common sense and the ability to achieve health and happiness in life.

Older Children

In traditional countries, the order of the universe was used to comprehend the cycles of human life. In one cycle, girls were understood to begin a new phase every seven years and boys every eight years. The differences in time span are based on the physiological differences between the sexes. Women, for example, have fewer red blood cells than men (about 4.5 million per cubic millimeter compared to about 5 million per cubic millimeter), a smaller average body size, and a heart rate that averages about seven beats per minute faster. Women change more rapidly than men. Puberty, for example, begins about two years earlier in girls than in boys.

The age of seven in girls and eight in boys marks the beginning of a new cycle of development. It lasts until fourteen in girls and sixteen in boys and includes the onset of puberty. In the past, it was normal for puberty to start later than it does today. For girls to begin puberty at fourteen and boys at sixteen was not unusual. Today, however, it typically begins at age ten in girls and twelve in boys. Some children begin even younger: there are many cases of girls beginning as early as seven. The increasing consumption of animal food in the twentieth century is the most prevalent factor contributing to the drop in the age of puberty. In Oriental countries, however, it was believed that early puberty was not necessarily advantageous. Later maturity was traditionally considered to be more favorable for health and well-being. In the sections that follow, we discuss some of the changes that occur during the latter part of childhood.

Permanent Teeth

The appearance of permanent teeth indicates that a child's organs and bodily systems are becoming increasingly like those of adults. Permanent teeth begin to appear around the age of six when the first molars appear behind the baby molars. They continue to come in until the third molars or wisdom teeth appear, usually between ages seventeen and twenty-one. Children lose their twenty baby teeth during this time and acquire thirty-two adult teeth. The adult teeth are usually completed by the age of twelve to fourteen, with the exception of the four wisdom teeth.

The adult teeth correspond to the vertebrae in the spine and also to all of the major organs and glands. When a permanent tooth appears, it shows that the organ it corresponds to has achieved a greater degree of maturity. The permanent teeth normally appear in the following order:

Table 6

Age	Tooth	Location	Corresponding Organs and Functions
6–7	First molars or "six-year" molars (4)	Behind baby teeth	Lower digestive vessel, especially ascending colon
7–9	Incisors (8)	In place of first incisors (8)	Respiratory and circulatory organs and glands
8–10	Premolars (8)	In place of first molars (8)	Upper intestinal region; excretory system
10–13	Canines (4)	In place of first canines (4)	Liver, gallbladder, spleen, pancreas, stomach
	Second molars or "twelve-year" molars (4)	Behind first molars	Lower digestive vessel, especially transverse colon
17–21	Third molars or "wisdom teeth" (4)	Behind second molars	Lower digestive vessel, especially descending colon

When a child has trouble with permanent teeth it is generally because of imbalances in the diet during the time that they are coming in. Food is a primary factor influencing the size, shape, quality, spacing, and angle of the teeth, including their resistance or susceptibility to decay. A naturally balanced diet furthers the growth and maintenance of strong and healthy teeth. The modern diet—rich in simple sugars, refined flour, and dairy and other animal products—contributes to a wide range of tooth and gum disorders. Problems with the teeth are related to the quality and functioning of the organs and systems that they correspond to. (For a discussion of what the teeth reveal about one's internal condition, please refer to *How to See Your Health: The Book of Oriental Diagnosis*, by the author.)

Growth Patterns

Physical growth tends to slow down during the latter part of childhood. The rate of growth becomes logarithmically slower from birth until puberty. The most rapid increase of course occurs before birth, when the rate of growth in inches per year is about twenty. This slows to about half or about ten inches during the first year and again to half, or about five inches, during the second year. Growth continues to slow down during the third and fourth years, reaching about half, or between two and three inches per year, at age five. This slower rate of growth continues until puberty at which time, growth accelerates. This acceleration in growth is known as the *adolescent growth spurt* and in many children today it occurs between ages nine and twelve in girls and between ages eleven and fourteen in boys. Growth during the years of seven to ten, just before puberty, is generally the slowest of any time during childhood.

The rate of growth does not remain constant throughout the year but alternates from season to season. Children tend to grow taller in the spring and fatter in the fall. Diets tend to become lighter or more expansive in the spring, and this produces more vertical growth. In the autumn and winter, they become more yang or contractive, and also include more proteins and fats. This causes more horizontal growth.

Boys and girls generally grow at about the same rates until around the ages of seven and eight. It is at this time that differences between the sexes become increasingly pronounced. Girls are more yang at birth and tend to be attracted to more yin proteins, liquids, fats, and carbohydrates during childhood. As a result, they tend to gain more fat during their adolescent period. Boys are more yin at birth and tend to be attracted to more yang minerals, proteins, and carbohydrates during childhood and thus experience a greater degree of muscle and bone growth during adolescence. The more yin components in a girl's diet tend to be attracted to the lower abdomen, buttocks, and thighs, producing the characteristic triangle of the female form (△). The more yang components in a boy's diet tend to be attracted toward the shoulders, causing the upper body to become more well-developed. This produces the characteristic triangle of the male form (▽).

Emotional, Intellectual, and Social Development

As physical growth slows down just before puberty a child's mental development accelerates. Children associate with teachers, playmates, and friends, and their scope of interaction continues to widen. They become interested in the outside world and in their relationship to it and are more keenly aware of male and female differences. Toddlers and young children often have playmates of both sexes, but during the latter part of childhood they usually make more friends of the same sex.

The latter part of childhood is ideal for learning, study, and the development of intellectual and artistic abilities, as well as for the development of physical strength and coordination. Children can become actively involved in reading, writing, mathematics, cooking, music, art, sports, and other activities that challenge them mentally and physically.

In many traditional cultures, boys and girls were educated separately. The separation of sexes was often continued through primary and secondary school, and in many colleges. Many traditional educators felt that the separation made it easier for young people to concentrate on their studies and to develop a strong sense of identity.

Children in the middle years are in a stage of transition from toddlers to teenagers. They change from being completely dependent upon their parents to being more independent. They develop a longer span of concentration, more fluent speech, greater physical agility and control, the ability to reflect on themselves and on their actions, and to regulate their emotions and behavior. Their thinking becomes deeper, involving larger areas of the brain than in early childhood, and they begin seeking explanations for many of the things they see around them. As children begin school and leave the home on a regular basis, they are exposed to many outside influences and begin comparing them to the attitudes, dreams and patterns of daily life that they have learned at home. They become increasingly sensitive to the way that others see them.

Children also develop the ability to take responsibility for small chores around the house, such as keeping their rooms clean, helping in the kitchen or in the garden or lawn, and helping out with younger brothers and sisters. They also do not seek or require the more constant care and attention they did at a younger age, and begin taking initiative in expanding their horizons. They want to demonstrate—to themselves as well as others—greater independence by doing things like walking to school by themselves, riding their bicycles without supervision, crossing the street, and playing outside with their friends.

However, even though children act more independently, they still look to parents for approval and guidance. What they learn at home forms the basis of how they evaluate society. Parents, brothers and sisters, and other family members can help them to understand the many things they encounter in society and cope with and overcome any failures, disappointments, and rejections that they experience. Some children may begin to question the values or practices that they learned at home as a result of being exposed to new ideas and ways of doing things. It is important for parents to be sensitive to the many questions that children have and to address them with love and understanding.

In the chapters that follow, we discuss some of the practical aspects of child care, starting with the foundation of proper diet and daily care for health and well-being, and including developing a healthy, loving, and supportive home environment.

Chapter **3**

Diet and Daily Care

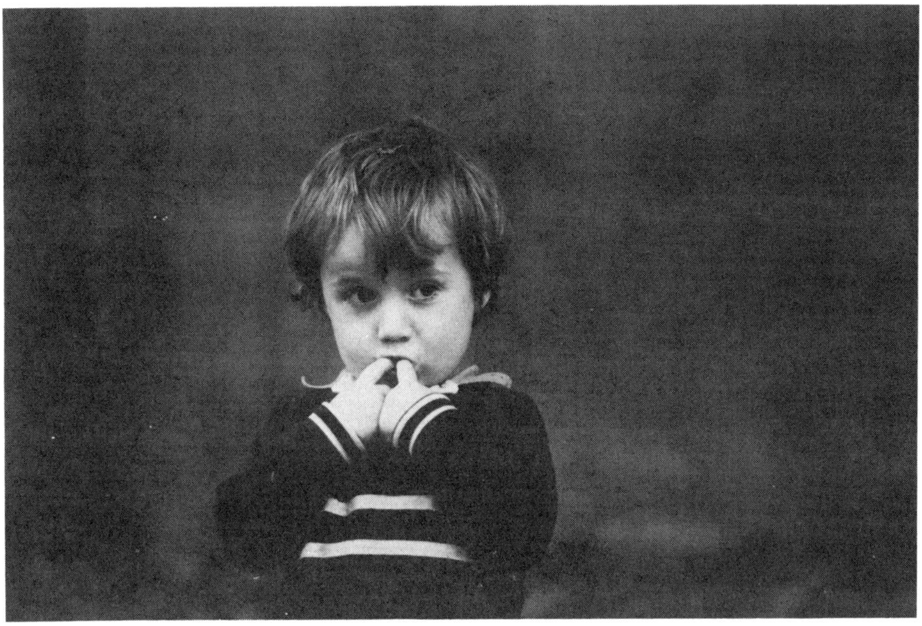

There is a proverb in the Orient: "The soul of three years lasts a hundred years." This traditional belief reflects the idea that whatever children learn in their first three years will influence them throughout life. The parents' character and lifestyle have a tremendous impact on their children. If the father and mother are happy, loving, and positive about life, their children will probably assume a similar attitude. If they quarrel or have a negative outlook, their children can easily grow into quarrelsome or negative adults.

Children are often mirror images of their parents. If parents spend their evenings watching television, for example, their children will probably grow to imitate them. Similarly, adults who behave in an offensive way may find their children copying their manner. A baby watches her parents very carefully. They are crucial models for her development. When children behave in an unacceptable way, parents must recognize their influence and responsibility.

If profanity is used at home, parents should not be surprised if children start to use the same words. When adults use elegant and respectful language, children tend to develop a similar way of speaking. People who are spiritually developed do not use profanity. They prefer more elegant and respectful language.

Education begins at home. Guiding children to become healthy, loving, and happy adults is one of the joys and responsibilities of parenthood. Home education is a joyful, loving process. It ideally includes the following aspects:

1. *Encouraging natural curiosity.* Children are always seeking to learn, to know, and to understand. Encourage this natural curiosity. It is easy to misunderstand a child's questioning. When a child asks, "Mommy, how did I come here?" a mother may blush and say, "Ask daddy." When she asks her father, he may say, "You're too young to know about these things. When you start school, ask your teacher." Later, if she asks the teacher, the teacher may say, "Your parents will discuss the facts of life with you when you're old enough. Better get busy with your math and reading."

   In this case, parents may think that the child is asking about sex, but what she really wants to know is how she came to be born on this earth. She may be seeking answers to very large questions. If parents respond to this curiosity, they can help a child develop insight, a rich imagination, and a large view of life. Try to use simple, clear, and poetic language when explaining things to children. The simpler and clearer, the better.

   "How" and "why" are two things that children always want to know. However, they are usually not answered in school. If, for example, a child questions why one and one equals two, he or she would probably be thought strange. Or, if a child were to ask a science teacher, "Why does gravity exist?" the teacher would probably answer, "Simply because it does."

   Children are required to memorize a great deal of information in school, but are rarely encouraged to ask "how" or "why." Since these questions are usually ignored, the natural curiosity that children possess is usually extinguished by the time they finish school. As a result, adults often do not know the answers to the most fundamental questions of life or how to solve such basic problems as what to eat to keep their health.

   When children come with questions, encourage them to think and discover solutions for themselves. We should use our understanding of the order of the universe and nature to point them in a direction. Parents can judge their own understanding by the way that children react to their explanations. If our expression is dry and conceptual, children will let us know by rapidly losing interest. If our expression is clear and dynamic, children will become attentive listeners.

2. *Encouraging children's dreams and ambitions.* Whatever children hope to do, parents should encourage them to follow through with their ambitions. If they want to play the piano, garden, learn to cook, study physics, or whatever, support them totally. Nourish their aspirations and grow with them.

   When Michio came to America, he did a variety of odd jobs such as washing dishes and working as a bellboy. He wrote often to his parents in Japan. They had trouble understanding why he was doing such things after having graduated from Tokyo University, which is the top university in

Japan. They expected him to be more like his classmates who were climbing the corporate ladder or making places for themselves in the fields of education and government. Both of his parents were educators, and they wondered why he was not pursuing a similar career.

More than fifteen years after Michio left Japan, his parents came to America with the hope of convincing him to return. They worried about him. They believed that had he remained in Japan, he would have become far more successful. They stayed in our home in Cambridge, Massachusetts, where we gave evening classes for a small group of students. When class finished, Michio would go down to the basement to pack brown rice, azuki beans, miso, and other macrobiotic staples. This small business eventually grew into Erewhon, one of the largest distributors of natural foods in the world.

For two weeks, his parents observed our actions without comment. Finally, one morning, they said, "Michio, we would like to talk to you this evening." We expected them to ask us to return to Japan. We knew they were acting out of love, and could not think of a way of refusing them, even though we had committed ourselves to continuing our macrobiotic activities in America.

That night, they attended the class. They sat in their usual place at the back of the room and kept silent. When the class finished, they waited until everyone left and then closed the door. Michio steadied himself. Suddenly, to his complete surprise, they knelt in front of him and bowed. Then his mother said, "Michio, we want to become your students," and added, "I don't know much about macrobiotics yet, or about what you are teaching. But if you ever need someone to test whether or not what you are saying is true, let me be that person. I don't mind giving my life for your dream. Your father and I support you completely."

A similar thing happened when we visited Japan almost ten years later. We went to the Kushi family temple described in Chapter One and met with a large group of relatives, many of them elderly, including several in their nineties. We spoke for close to three hours. The following morning, several relatives came to our room and said, "Everyone who listened to you yesterday has decided to begin macrobiotics. They would like to become your students."

We experienced a joy similar to the one we felt when Michio's parents recognized our activities many years before. We felt very thankful to be part of such a wonderful family. Our parents and relatives have inspired us to return our happiness unconditionally to others.

As these stories show, the love and encouragement of parents and seniors are so important for children's happiness. Nourishing the dreams and ambitions of children can be far more important than giving them money or possessions. Encourage children to pursue their hopes and ambitions.

3. *Honesty.* During the Russo-Japanese War, Japan's naval forces were led by

a man named Admiral Tōgō. Even though it was relatively unsophisticated, the Japanese Navy overcame tremendous odds and managed to destroy the Russian Navy in the seas around Japan.

Admiral Tōgō never sought fame or personal glory. He was a traditional *samurai*. He often told stories, including one about lying. When he was a boy, his mother would occasionally give him a piece of rice candy as a treat. She kept the candy in a jar on a high shelf in the closet. One day, he asked her for a piece of candy and she told him there wasn't any. That afternoon, when she left the house, he went straight to the closet and piled up cushions so he could reach the jar. He found several pieces of candy there and climbed out and ate them. On the following day, his mother went to the closet to get him a piece of candy and discovered the empty jar. She asked if he stole the candy and he replied, "No, I didn't. There wasn't any candy left. You told me so." His mother was quiet for a moment. Then she knelt down in front of him. She bowed and said, "I was wrong. I'm sorry that I lied to you. It was my fault and I'll never lie to you again." At that moment he understood how wrong it was to lie. He also saw what a wonderful spirit his mother had. The experience created a deep love and respect for his mother, and taught him a lesson that influenced his adult life.

If, instead of self-reflecting, she had tried to conceal her mistake or had attacked or criticized her son, his attitude would have been very different. Her approach had a deep and long-lasting effect; Admiral Tōgō was known throughout his life as an extremely honest man.

Parents are encouraged to keep their promises to children. If we tell children that we will take them to a museum or buy them a new toy, we should be sure to do what we say. If we break our word, children will learn to distrust us. Breaking promises is a form of lying. Therefore, be careful not to make promises that cannot be kept.

4. *A modest lifestyle.* Modesty is very important. It is better to keep food, clothing, and everyday items as simple and natural as possible. An abundance of rich foods or material goods or an overly protective environment can make a child weak. Children who are spoiled often cannot cope with difficulties and problems later in life.

Many great people grew up in humble surroundings where they learned to be moderate. Many leaders were taught from childhood to be modest. In Japan, for example, the *Shōgun* received a very strict education. As a child, he would accompany samurai and other adults on hunting trips. In the evening, the adults would sit around a campfire eating the wild game caught during the day. The mood was festive, with plenty of eating and drinking. However, the future Shōgun was not allowed to participate. Instead of enjoying the wild game, he had to eat more humble fare such as roasted brown rice and pickles.

The members of the Imperial Family received similar training. The Crown Prince was not permitted to sit in a chair or on cushions if anyone in his party had to stand. He could not eat white rice, sugar, or other refined foods. Because of this custom, the diet of the Imperial Family has remained simple. Even today, the members of the Emperor's family eat brown rice, fresh garden vegetables, miso soup, pickles, and sea vegetables.

After the war, some people began to feel that it was unfair for the Emperor not to be able to enjoy meat, cheese, sugar, and other luxury items. It was even suggested that he stop eating brown rice and, like most Japanese, begin to eat white rice. The Emperor understood their feelings but very politely told them that he preferred to continue to eat brown rice. Someone then suggested that brown rice did not taste as good as white rice, and was more difficult to chew. Even though he disagreed, the Emperor finally compromised by eating a mixture of partially polished rice and barley in order to please his people. He felt it improper to eat completely polished rice, regardless of public opinion. The diet of the Imperial Family is now more humble than that of the average Japanese family.

5. *Letting children help around the house.*   Children are often eager to help with household chores. They enjoy working with their parents, brothers and sisters, and other people in the home. When children express the desire to participate, let them do so. They can help with cooking, cleaning, taking out the trash, and other chores that are suitable for their age. Encourage children to take part in your daily routines.

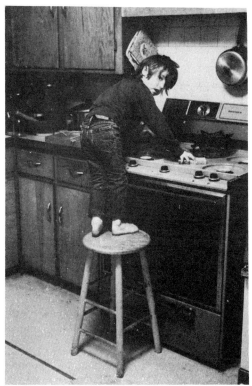

6. *Establishing order in family relations.*   It is important to treat the younger members of the family with love and care. Grown-ups need to view children with patience and understanding, although their behavior may at times seem disorderly or immature. We should also show respect and love for the elders in our family even if, at times, we disagree with their opinions. When parents receive elder guests in their home with politeness and respect, children learn to extend similar courtesy to teachers and other seniors in society. Children observe how their parents relate to others and imitate what they see.

Age distinctions are often blurred by language. The pronouns "you" or "I," for example, are used in English regardless of a person's age. We address a three-year-old child as "you," and do the same with a seventy-year-old grandmother. A second grader refers to himself as "I," and so does a retired grandfather. Parents address their children as "you," and children do likewise when addressing their parents. Some people even address their parents by their first names. However, other languages often utilize a variety of pronouns for different occasions. In Japanese, for example, more polite forms are used when addressing an older person, and informal words are used when speaking to peers or juniors. Ideally, language should acknowledge differences in age and it is better if we relate to children in a way that is a little different from the way we relate to our parents and elders.

7. *Family events.*   Today, people tend to pursue their own interests, and often do not involve their parents, children, or other members of their families in what they do; whereas in the past, families shared or discussed their experiences regularly. They usually met everyday for the main meal and frequently prayed or attended religious services together. Holidays were also times when kinfolk would gather to give thanks and enjoy festive dishes.

As we have said, it is important for families to eat together at least once a day. But besides eating, it is important to take time to do a variety of other things together. Holidays and birthdays are wonderful occasions for family gatherings. Grandparents, brothers and sisters, and other relatives not living at home can be invited to these events. A variety of special party foods can be enjoyed by everyone.

Picnics, outings to the beach or countryside, concerts, movies, or visits to museums are only a few possible family activities. Reading stories to children in the evening is also very enjoyable. If someone in your family plays a musical instrument, your whole family can enjoy an informal concert or group sing along.

Events that involve the whole family bolster confidence and increase cooperation and harmony. They help members realize that they are supported by a larger group.

Creating a family is a marvelous thing. We could have been born on one of millions of other planets in the universe; or could have been born a thousand years ago or a million years from now. But we as individuals, our husband or wife, our parents, children, and brothers and sisters chose this planet at this time. Our relationship to the people in our family and to our friends is truly precious.

The possibility of developing unconditional love is present within every family. Families are microcosms of the order of the universe in which the laws of love and harmony continually work. The members of a family share blood and spirit, yet each member is unique. The complementarity that exists between husband and wife, parents and children, brothers and sisters, and seniors and juniors broadens and deepens the underlying harmony. A family is like a stream that flows through time and space. Growth, learning, sharing, and loving are all part of the stream. Joy and sadness, difficulty and happiness, and youth and old age are waves that come and go. Yet the stream continually flows on and becomes a mighty river.

To guide children toward health and happiness is the work of God. It is far more important than building an empire or acquiring a billion dollars. Even if you conquer the world, you have not fully developed if you are unable to create a happy and healthy family. The health and happiness of your family is a barometer of your spiritual development. Titles such as King, Emperor, Scientist, President, or Professor are only human creations, whereas a happy and healthy family is the creation of the universe itself.

Making your family healthy and happy is a direct contribution to world health and world peace. What we do for our families is equivalent to our contribution to the world. There is really no difference between the health and well-being of your family and that of your community, nation, and the world. Educating children to become healthy, productive, and fulfilled adults will produce positive benefits for humanity now and in the future. Our children are our future. How this future unfolds is up to us.

Children's Food

When babies reach the age of six to eight months, their first teeth begin to appear. Weaning can be begun at this time by gradually introducing solid foods. Some babies may show an interest in eating solid foods before this time, but as a general rule most are not so interested. Since babies are very yang and grow rapidly, it is important that their foods be very light and softly cooked. Use a larger proportion of water than for adult foods and do not include salt in the beginning. After baby foods have been cooked over a low flame until soft, they can be placed in a suribachi or a hand baby food mill and puréed. Cereals can be made a little more yin by adding a very small amount of grain sweetener such as good quality barley malt or rice syrup on occasion.

Until the age of six to eight months, when the baby's teeth first appear, they can be fed breast milk only.[1] When the teeth begin to come in, decrease the

---

[1] For suggestions concerning what to do when there is a lack of breast milk, please refer to *Macrobiotic Pregnancy and Care of the Newborn* by the authors, Japan Publications, Inc., 1984.

amount of breast milk very slowly while increasing the volume of softly cooked solid foods.

The first foods that we introduce to the baby are whole cereal grains, beginning with rice, which is cooked very softly, mildly seasoned with the sweeteners mentioned above, and puréed to a very thin creamy consistency. Introduce other grains one at a time. Let the baby get used to each for about a week before introducing another grain. Gradually add different grains over several weeks, to make a wide variety for the baby. If we introduce too many foods at once, babies may become confused and refuse to eat any solid foods and return only to breast milk.

Figure 6   General Guidelines for Feeding Children

Age in months	Front Teeth	First Molar																		Second Molar
0 1 2 3 4 5 6 7	8 9 10 11 12	13 14 15 16 17 18 19 20 21 22 23 24 25																		
Mother's Milk	Milk / Soft Food	Soft Food (Plain Taste) / Harder Food (Gradual Salt Taste)																	Hard Food →

After the baby has been eating whole cereal grains for about two to three weeks, begin to gradually introduce vegetables like broccoli, carrots, squash, cabbage, onions, and kale, and sea vegetables such as kombu and wakame. These can be cooked and mashed together with the grains. It is recommended that softly cooked whole cereal grains of different varieties comprise at least half of the baby's intake.

Many times we are not careful enough in weaning babies properly and gradually. All children are different and must be weaned according to their individual needs and preferences. Most babies can be fully weaned by the age of one to one-and-a-half. Weaning a baby too soon may cause emotional as well as digestive problems, while weaning too late may cause the child to be overly dependent on the mother.

As the child becomes older the volume of water used in cooking can be gradually reduced. Slowly begin to give the child foods that have a consistency similar to adult foods, but that are still slightly softer and very mildly seasoned. By the time a child is about four years old, he or she can generally eat most of the foods an adult eats but more mildly seasoned. By the time children are about eight years old they usually can eat whatever is served for adults. However, if some adult dishes are very strong or salty, it may be best to prepare a small volume for children with less salt. Until the child becomes an adult it is wise to be very careful of strong or salty tasting dishes.

Throughout childhood parents will want to observe what each child eats daily and notice how they react to various foods. By doing this parents can learn how to cook for their children, what their likes and dislikes are, how to handle any imbalances or sickness, and how to create happy and healthy children.

Specific suggestions for introducing solid foods are listed below:

- *Whole Cereal Grains*—Brown rice is usually the first cereal grain that is given to babies. It is very easy to digest and babies generally like its taste. Rice is also the most balanced whole grain in terms of nutrients.

  Cereals can be introduced around the age of six to eight months. Babies can be given cereals that are cooked with about five to seven times more water than grain. No salt should be added to the grain until around the age of one to one-and-a-half years. Instead of sea salt add a one-inch piece of kombu to the grains when cooking.

  The main grains for babies are brown rice, barley, and sweet brown rice. Millet can be used from time to time also. Some children with a more yin or frail constitution may be able to eat a very small amount of buckwheat, while a more yang or sturdy baby may become excessively yang from eating it. Buckwheat is generally not given to babies under normal circumstances. Wheat, rye, and flint corn are more difficult to digest and are not usually recommended. Corn on the cob may be given in the summer or fresh corn may be mixed with rice. All grains are soaked prior to cooking to help make them softer and more digestible.

  Cook a baby's cereals in their whole form. Do not grind them into flour before cooking, as the child needs the whole energy of the grain in order to digest it properly. Cracked cereals are also best avoided. After cooking grains in their whole form, they can be placed in a suribachi or baby food mill and puréed to make them easy to swallow and more digestible.

  Slowly begin reducing the amount of water used in making children's grains over a period of two to three years. When preparing cereals for a baby six to ten months old, use five to seven times more water than grain. For a one year old, use three to four times more water than grain. By the time children are four years old, their whole grain dishes are just slightly softer than those of adults. As the volume of water is reduced, also reduce the amount of grinding and puréeing in preparing food. Eventually, mashing the food with a fork to make it soft should be enough, rather than milling or puréeing it.

If we continue to feed the child very soft or watery foods longer than necessary without giving enough finger foods or foods of firmer consistency, the child's intestines may become weak. If the intestines do not function properly, a child may not obtain enough nutrients from daily foods. By the time children are one-and-a-half to two years old, they can eat primarily softly cooked but unpuréed foods or finger foods such as soft cooked vegetables, *sushi*, small rice balls, or unsalted rice cakes. Noodles and fu can be introduced around the age of ten months.

● *Soups*—Soups or vegetable broths may be introduced after six to seven months. They may include vegetables cooked with either wakame or kombu sea vegetable. Soups can be cooked until the ingredients are very soft and then puréed for a creamy consistency. Sea salt and tamari are best not added until children are about one to one-and-a-half. Mildly seasoned soups, including light miso soup, can be given after the age of two.

● *Vegetables*—Vegetables can be introduced approximately one month after the baby has been eating whole cereal grains and has adjusted smoothly to them. It is best to begin by introducing the sweeter vegetables such as squash, carrots, cabbage, onions, daikon, Chinese cabbage, and broccoli. Children do not particularly care to eat foods that have a bitter, sour, or hot taste. Sweet tasting round, ground, or root vegetables are best. Babies often have difficulties chewing and digesting hard fibrous leafy greens, so it is better to use those which are softer and less tough such as broccoli, cabbage, Chinese cabbage, or kale. Many times children do not enjoy eating leafy greens, so a special effort must be made to ensure that they do eat some. Greens may have to be mixed in with a child's grain or soup.

● *Beans*—Beans can be introduced after one to one-and-a-half years, but many babies do not care for them until they are about two. It is very important not to give too many beans as they can be difficult for a baby's young intestines to digest, and may create digestive problems if eaten too often. Beans can be cooked with kombu to help soften their hard shells and to make them more digestible. Beans can be well cooked and thoroughly mashed before being served to babies. Give them in very small quantities only. Chick-peas, azuki beans, and lentils can be introduced for more regular use, along with kidney, navy, and other suitable beans for occasional use.

Tofu and dried tofu can be included in their diet when children are about ten months to one year old. Tempeh can be served after one-and-a-half to two years. Tempeh makes children very energetic and for this reason it is recommended that it be very mildly seasoned and cooked slowly over a low flame until it is very soft and easily digestible. It is better to give children only a very small amount of tempeh.

• *Sea Vegetables*—Wakame and kombu are usually the first sea vegetables to be introduced. Kombu can be cooked in with grains in place of sea salt. It can also be cooked together with root vegetables or nishime dishes. Kombu or wakame can also be used in preparing soups, and, as we have said, kombu can also be cooked in with beans. It is much easier for a baby to eat sea vegetables if they are cooked with other foods.

Sea vegetables such as arame and hijiki are usually not included in grain and bean dishes, but can be cooked with vegetables such as carrots, squash, onions, or dried daikon. Sea vegetable side dishes are mashed and served in very small quantities. Arame and hijiki can be introduced after a child is one to one-and-a-half years old. Because roasted nori is soft and easy to eat, children often like to snack on it. Nori can be introduced around the age of one, but be careful not to overdo it. Sea vegetables are naturally salty and contain many minerals. Children can become too yang if they eat too large a volume.

• *Fruits, Sweets and Fish*—As mentioned in Chapter One, fruits, sweets and fish are supplementary foods and are usually not recommended for daily consumption. Locally grown, temperate climate fruits can be cooked, mashed, and given to children over the age of one to one-and-a-half. Young children can have a small serving three or four times a week on the average. It is ideal to give babies good quality grain sweeteners more often than fruit sweets. Offer children grain puddings or warm amazaké, or add a little grain sweetener to their cereal from time to time. A few raisins can be sprinkled on top of their breakfast cereal on occasion. Some mothers think that babies should be given fruits from the beginning, but this is actually unnecessary. It is best not to force children to eat fruits or give them to children too soon. Sweet tasting vegetable and grain dishes are preferable.[2]

Although fish is usually unnecessary for regular consumption, a small volume can be introduced after a child is one-and-a-half to two years old. A very small portion of white-meat, non-fatty fish may be given from time to time, on an average of once a week. If you notice that fish makes your child very aggressive or irritable it may be better to avoid it or serve it only on rare

---

[2] Kanten is a very nice dessert for children, but it is better if they do not eat too much of it at one time or have it too often. It is also better for children to eat kanten at room temperature rather than icy cold. Warm or room temperature amazaké is also better than chilled amazaké. Always remember that rice balls, mochi, noodles, and raw carrots or celery are enjoyable as snacks. These snacks do not cause problems with childrens' health. It is important for children not to eat desserts before they go to bed. It is better for children to have them during the day or early in the evening.—*Aveline Kushi.*

occasions such as holidays. Some children will not eat fish until the age of two or three, while others may refuse to eat it until they are older.

- *Quick, Light Pickles*—Light pickles or mild pressed salads may be introduced after a child is two to three years old. They should be very lightly salted and preferably have a sweet taste. They are best given in very small quantities only.

- *Beverages*—During the time that babies are breast-feeding only, it is usually unnecessary to give them anything else to drink. When weaning begins, a baby may be given very mild, weak bancha or grain teas. Do not force babies to drink if they are not thirsty. Remember that babies are getting liquid in the form of breast milk and, if being weaned, in the softly cooked foods they receive. If children are thirsty, give them a small amount to drink, but do not force them. Children over a year old can occasionally have a little warm apple juice or amazaké that has been diluted in water or a combination of apple juice and bancha or grain tea.

  Bubbly or carbonated waters can be enjoyed by older children on rare occasions. Be careful, though, not to give them to children too often. It is better to let children drink the fresh spring or well water that we use in daily cooking. They can also enjoy apple or carrot juice from time to time, but watch their condition closely to see how it affects them.

- *Oil*—We can start to use a very small amount of high quality sesame or corn oil very occasionally after a child is about two. However, it is best to wait until children are about five before giving them oil on a regular basis.

  Oil is difficult to digest unless it is cooked with salt. As babies or small children should have only tiny amounts of salt until they are two to three years old, it is necessary to limit their use of oil. Natural oils can be obtained from grains, beans, and bean products, as well as from breast milk. Be very careful when introducing oil. When used excessively, it can cause a rash on the face or can even cause a fever. It can also be a primary cause of diarrhea or green colored stools. When we do begin to introduce oil, it is a good idea to serve a small amount of boiled red radish or boiled dried daikon at the same meal. They can be cooked together with grains or other vegetables or used in soups. They help the child to digest oil.

- *Seasonings*—Sea salt can be introduced after the age of one to one-and-a-half. Only one or two grains of salt can be added to grain or vegetable dishes. Gradually increase the amount of salt in a child's diet, over a period of several years. An eight- to ten-year-old can usually take the normal adult food, but some dishes may need to be seasoned more mildly. A very small amount of tamari can be introduced in cooking after a child is one-and-a half to two years old, while very light and mild miso soups can be introduced after two years of age. Tamari should be used in cooking and not as a condiment by children (or adults).

  Children are usually able to eat the standard macrobiotic diet by the age of four or five, with a very moderate use of salt, condiments, pickles, and oil.

Fish is generally unnecessary as a daily item but may be enjoyed occasionally in small amounts by older children. It is generally better to avoid giving items such as fish, ginger, scallions, raw daikon, or other strong tasting foods to babies or infants. A mild, naturally sweet taste such as that of grains and vegetables is used most frequently in preparing baby foods.

● *Condiments*—Condiments that contain sea salt may be introduced after the age of one to one-and-a-half. However, they are best used only occasionally rather than on a daily basis, and in very tiny amounts. They can gradually be used more often and in slightly larger amounts as children grow. As with seasonings, children can generally use adult-strength condiments by the age of ten, but the use of salt is something that parents must continually monitor to prevent excess. It is better not to give children stronger condiments like *tekka*, *shio-kombu*, very strong pickles, salt sauerkraut, and umeboshi paste. Some children may develop a taste for tamari soy sauce, and may want to use it on noodles or in other dishes. Parents need to watch this very carefully. It is better if children do not get into the habit of using tamari as a condiment, especially on their rice or other cereals. If they occasionally use a few drops on noodles, fu, or mochi, it is recommended that parents be sure they use only a very tiny amount.

In our other book on family health, *Macrobiotic Pregnancy and Care of the Newborn*, we present a list of symptoms that may indicate an excessive intake of salt or an overly constricted condition. Since these signs are very important, and require immediate attention if they occur at any time during childhood, we have decided to include them here.

Parents can suspect an overly yang condition if children display any of the following signs:

1. Constant hunger or desire to eat.
2. Screaming. When a child screams, it is often a sign of an overly yang condition. Whining is an opposite type of crying and usually means that a child is too yin.
3. Tightness, lack of flexibility, or lack of motion.
4. Loss of the ability to crawl or walk.
5. The development of bowed legs, as in rickets.
6. Failure to grow. If a child is small at birth, for example five or six pounds, it is not necessarily a cause for concern. Smaller babies often have more vitality and capacity for growth than oversized babies. After birth, however, children normally grow very rapidly. Too much salt can inhibit growth and cause children to remain small and contracted.
7. Poor circulation. Salt can cause the peripheral capillaries to contract and inhibit blood flow. Cold hands or feet or a pale color may indicate this problem.
8. Abnormal weight. There is no fixed rate at which children gain weight.

The standard height and weight charts that are commonly used today are often unreliable. The growth rates on these charts tend to reflect averages among formula-fed children. Normal ranges for breast-fed children, or for children who eat macrobiotically have not yet been developed. Some children gain weight more rapidly, others more slowly. Babies who are smaller at birth tend to gain rapidly, while larger infants tend to gain more slowly. As children get older, their rate of physical growth tends to slow down before adolescence.

As long as children have good appetites, parents need not be overly concerned about their weight. However, if children become abnormally thin or fat, it may be a sign of too much salt or a sign of some other imbalance in daily diet. An excessive intake of salt can cause a child to contract and become tight and skinny. In some cases, it can cause a child to retain water, fat, and other more yin substances and to become overweight.

9. Dry or rough skin. Children normally have soft and smooth skin.
10. A change in bowel movement toward dark or hard stools. The bowel movement is one of the most important things to check when trying to determine whether a child's condition is too yin, too yang, or in balance.

Figure 7   Qualities of Bowel Movement Color and Consistency

	black	brown	yellow	gray/ white	green	black/ purple
watery						
very soft						
soft						
solid						
hard & granular						

The yin and yang classification of children's bowel movements is presented in the chart above. Color and consistency are the two main factors to consider. A soft, yellow bowel movement is best for nursing infants. As children get older, the bowel movement normally becomes more yellowish-brown and firmer in consistency. If children have frequent green and watery stools, their condition is chronically out of balance. A child who eats macrobiotically normally has one bowel movement per day. The stools of macrobiotic children do not have an unpleasant odor.

11. In rare cases, a high fever. Fevers caused by too much salt are not as common as the other symptoms presented here. Please refer to the follow-

ing chapter for a discussion of the other dietary imbalances that cause fever.

12. Irregular appetite. As stated above, salt can cause children to eat excessive amounts of food. However, salt can also cause the appetite to diminish because of its constrictive effect on the digestive organs.

When any of these symptoms occur, or if you suspect an overly contracted condition in a child (these symptoms can also result from the overintake of baked flour products or from a lack of variety—including fresh, leafy greens—in the diet), the child's diet needs adjusting. The first step toward a more natural balance is to limit the child's intake of excessively yang foods. Try reducing or temporarily avoiding the use of salt in cooking the child's dishes. Non-salty condiments can be used in place of salty ones. The naturally sweet taste can be relied on more than usual. Grains such as sweet rice or oats, which are fattier than brown rice, barley, or millet, can be included more often. If necessary, the child's grain dishes can be prepared with a little more water than usual, so as to create a softer and creamier consistency. On occasion, a small amount of barley malt, rice syrup, amazaké, or raisins can be added to soft breakfast cereals. Puffed whole grain cereals can also be eaten with amazaké from time to time. Vegetables that become sweet when cooked—such as carrots, squash, cabbage, daikon, and onions—can be served to the child daily, together with lightly steamed greens, and pressed or boiled salads. A small amount of umeboshi or brown rice vinegar can be used as a seasoning when desired. Shiitake mushrooms can also be cooked with root vegetables, or frequently used in soups. The special shiitake tea mentioned in the discussion of fever in the following chapter can also be given on occasion, perhaps several times per week for a month or so.

It is better to use lightly cooked vegetable dishes to restore the child to balance rather than a large amount of fruit, liquids, or concentrated sweeteners. In this way the child can return to a more balanced condition without swinging out to the opposite extreme. A small amount of cooked apple, pear or other fruit sauce, apple juice, fruit kanten or compote, or a small piece of fresh northern fruit may be eaten on occasion. It is better to keep the intake moderate.

In addition to modifying the diet, the child may enjoy daily warm baths. Bathing helps the body discharge excess salt and minerals.

- *Gomashio* is normally a very good condiment for children. It is made from whole sesame seeds and sea salt. When made at home, you can freely adjust the proportion of seeds to salt to suit any age or condition. When making children's gomashio, grind the seeds a little more finely than you would for an adult. More finely crushed seeds are easier to digest. Put the toasted seeds into a suribachi and grind them until they are about 75 percent crushed. The ratio of salt to seeds can be about one to twenty-five. As children get older, gradually adjust the proportion of seeds to salt. It can be about one to fifteen by the age of ten. Condiments can also be made without salt. Plain toasted sesame or sunflower seeds are fine for children. A condiment can also be prepared with roasted sesame seeds and a small amount of roasted wakame sea vegetable. Roast the ingredients and then crush them in a suribachi as done when making gomashio.

● *Umeboshi* can be used medicinally for children with stomach trouble or other digestive upset. A very small piece can be put in their soft cereal. Be careful about the amount of umeboshi that children eat. Even when they are five or six, it is better to limit their intake to half of a plum on occasion. As with other condiments, if we notice a child becoming too tight, we can stop giving them umeboshi until their condition returns to normal.

If children eat something a little bit salty once in a while, such as a piece of pickle, there is usually no need to worry. But watch their condition to see how it affects them.

● *Sweet nori condiment* is very mild and is nice to give to children on occasion. Nori condiment can be sweetened by adding a little barley malt while it is being prepared. Children often enjoy rubbing a little umeboshi plum on their corn on the cob. Again, be sure they use only a small amount. When cooked, the taste of sauerkraut becomes milder and less salty. Milder sauerkraut is usually better for children. Ginger and other condiments with a spicy flavor are generally too strong for children.

● *Snacks*—Children have difficulty digesting oil. It is therefore best not to give them oily chips or snacks. Ideally, children eat items such as these on rare

occasions only. Crackers and cookies can be eaten once in a while but not often. Dry, baked flour products need a lot of chewing which is difficult for children. Also, the intake of dry baked foods tends to make children thirsty and causes them to drink more than usual. Rice cakes are better than hard dry crackers or cookies, and can be enjoyed with a little apple butter on them from time to time. Be careful not to give children too much nut butter or tahini. Seeds and nuts are difficult to digest without thorough chewing, and are best eaten only on occasion. Children can enjoy a few raw raisins once in a while. But even better is to cook them with a little *kuzu* (a starch made from a wild vine) or kuzu and fruit and serve them as a dessert. Raisins can also be occasionally cooked in cereals.

The ideal snacks for regular use are such foods as rice, vegetable, or noodle sushi, carrot and celery sticks, noodles or noodle salads, rice cakes, or other whole grain or vegetable items. Other snacks are best used only occasionally.

Eating Habits—Children's food should be tasty and attractive. If they are not hungry, however, do not force children to eat. If we do, they will usually end up playing with their food. It is best to serve children only small quantities of food at a time so that they do not waste any. If they want more give them small portions so that they finish what is on their plates. Remember that children do not require the same amount or volume of food that adults do. Encourage children to give thanks before and after each meal. Learning appreciation for food and the natural world that provides it, is good training for them.

Eating Problems

1. *When babies refuse to wean.* A mother can begin to wean her baby between the ages of one and one-and-a-half. Some children are very easy to wean, while others do not want to stop nursing. Each baby is different. If the baby refuses to be weaned, patience and common sense are called for. Sometimes a mother may need to be firm when offering solid food instead of breast milk. Remember, however, that weaning must be done gradually, until eventually the child is breast-feeding just once a day, at bedtime. If breast-feeding can be reduced to just once per day it is much easier to wean entirely. Weaning a baby without a gradual reduction in the number of feedings may result in the refusal to eat solid foods. If the baby foods that we prepare taste delicious and look appetizing, the weaning process will go more smoothly.

2. *When children refuse to eat by themselves.* When a baby first begins to eat solid foods, the mother will of course have to feed him. Most children quickly become interested in using a spoon and feeding themselves. The mother can teach them to do this properly without making too much of a mess. Some children may refuse to feed themselves because they feel insecure or neglected and want more attention. Try to figure out why your child is refusing to feed himself and

then correct the problem. In most cases children are naturally curious and want
to eat by themselves.

3. *Overeating.* As mentioned earlier, a common cause of overeating is the
overuse of salt, or the consumption of too many dry, baked flour products such
as cookies, bread, or crackers. When this occurs, reduce the intake of these items
and include more fresh and lightly cooked dishes.

4. *Under-eating.* Under-eating is often caused by a lack of variety in the diet.
Many children like to eat greens. However, it may sometimes be difficult to get
them to eat enough greens or other vegetables. Find out which vegetables children
like and let them have as much as they want. Then gradually increase their variety.
Sometimes we may have to disguise their vegetables by cooking them in soups
or grain dishes. Put vegetables in sushi or cut them in interesting shapes with
a cookie cutter or a knife. Practices such as these make it easier for children to
naturally begin to eat a variety of vegetables.

If a child eats too many snack foods, he may refuse to eat a well-balanced meal
of grains, vegetables, sea vegetables, beans, and other dishes. Mothers will want to
make sure that their children do not snack to the point of interfering with their
regular diet.

5. *School lunches.* Ideally, the school of the future will serve balanced, natural
food lunches prepared daily according to macrobiotic principles. Chefs will be
selected among persons who have studied macrobiotic cooking, and will work with
parents in determining daily meal plans. Parents will then not have to worry about
children eating junk foods or high fat, high sugar items while in school.

At present, however, parents cannot depend on the quality of foods offered in
school lunch programs. Here and there, some parents have interested schools in
including more natural items, but the public schools have generally been slow in
adapting a more natural nutritional approach.

A more sensible plan is for children to avoid unhealthful foods at school and
bring a lunch from home. If necessary, parents can meet with their child's teacher
or principal and explain why they wish to prepare their child's lunch. If school-
children enjoy a hearty breakfast, then they can usually get by with a lighter lunch.
Then, when they return from school in the afternoon, they can enjoy a light snack
of noodles, sushi, leftovers, fried rice or some other dish.

Sushi and rice balls are ideal foods for lunch boxes. So are sandwiches made
with whole grain breads. Carrot or celery sticks, lightly boiled or raw salads,
mochi, an occasional raw apple or piece of naturally sweetened pie, and other
simple dishes can also be included. Many of these items can be made to look like
the foods that other children take for lunch. Wholesome, natural dishes can be
made to resemble practically any food, so that children who bring a macrobiotic
lunch from home do not have to appear especially "different." Remember that a
growing number of families eat a more natural diet and many children bring

specially prepared lunches to school. Specific suggestions for preparing a variety of school lunches—including recipes and menus—are presented in *Macrobiotic Family Favorites* (see the Bibliography).

Daily Care

Sleeping—Parents are encouraged to observe each of their children to find out what each child's sleeping cycle is. Some may want to go to sleep early and wake up early, while others may want to stay up later and sleep later. Try not to force them to sleep earlier than they are generally used to as this may cause them to wake up very early in the morning. Waking up too early can be tiring for the parents. When children are very young they naturally want to go to bed early, but as they grow older their sleeping times need adjusting. At a young age they usually go to sleep around seven or eight o'clock and wake up around six or seven. Older children may go to bed between eight and nine and sleep until seven or eight. Once they are in school, some children may not want to go to bed early, but it is important that they go to bed at a reasonable hour so that they will be

alert and able to concentrate on their studies. Try different approaches to help them relax and go to sleep at an appropriate hour during school semesters. A warm bath, reading a book, telling them a story, or encouraging them to listen to relaxing music may calm children enough so that they feel sleepy.

Napping—When children are very young (under a year old), they usually take a nap in the morning and one later in the afternoon. As they grow older they may only take an afternoon nap. After the age of two or two-and-a-half, most children are no longer interested in taking a regular nap. Do not force a child to do so if

he does not want to sleep. When children are tired or need sleep, if their surroundings are made more calm and relaxing, they will go to sleep. After the age of three most children will nap only occasionally.

Sleeping Materials—We recommend that futons, mattresses, sheets, blankets, quilts, pillowcases, and other sleeping materials be made of high quality cotton. If a child still wets the bed at night, you can place a plastic or rubber sheet on top of the mattress, but always place a heavy cotton sheet over it so that the cotton is against the child's skin. Stop using the plastic sheet when the child stops bed-wetting. Sleepwear can also be made of high quality cotton material. Cotton is warm and comfortable while sleeping. It is better to use more loose fitting pajamas. Pajamas with attached socks or foot extensions are not recommended as they interfere with the circulation and often make children uncomfortable and unable to sleep properly. Instead of wearing pajamas with feet or wearing socks, it is better to simply cover the child with an extra blanket if necessary.

Sleeping Posture—In some parts of the world children sleep on their stomachs. However, we have observed that children sleep better and more soundly on their backs. If children are sick or not feeling comfortable for some reason, they will often sleep on their stomachs. But if they eat high quality food, prepared properly, they will sleep very well on their backs. Dinner is a very important meal for children. What is served for their evening meal can determine the time they go to sleep, how often they wake during the night, and what time they get up the next morning. It is better to serve foods that are easily digested for the evening meal. If a mother wishes to give her children snacks or desserts, it is better to serve them at lunch or sometime before dinner. If desserts are eaten too late in the evening they may not be easily digested and may cause problems with sleep.

If children eat fruit or drink juices in the evening, it may cause them to wet the bed. Try not to give children salty or oily foods at night as these can cause them to crave liquids. Drinking too much can then cause bed-wetting. It is better to give children foods that have the type of energy that will help them to hold in liquid while they sleep. Mochi or sweet vegetables are often good for this purpose.

Books, television, and movies also affect how children sleep. Parents must carefully select the books, television programs, and movies that children see or read. In fact it could be worthwhile for parents to see a movie first before taking their children to see it. The shows and cartoons on television are often violent or disturbing for youngsters. If children are allowed to watch such programs they may be afraid to go to sleep or may have nightmares. Books with ghosts, monsters, or other upsetting subjects in them are not recommended, especially not at night. We should be as careful in selecting their entertainment and reading material as we are in selecting their food. Children will be much happier as a result.

Waking Up—Some children wake up with a smile, some cry, and some are irritable. A child's mood may also vary from day to day. Children have different reactions to the foods they eat, the events of the previous day, and other factors in their environment. Try to see the connection between these factors and a child's condition when he or she wakes in the morning. Parents need to be happy, smiling, and pleasant when they wake children in the morning or after a nap. If we are annoyed that the child got up too early or if our greeting is not pleasant, the child may be upset the entire day or until we reassure him or her that we are not upset or annoyed. Some children are very hungry when they wake up and if their breakfast is not prepared quickly, they may become upset and irritable. Parents who do not always get up before or when their children do, can occasionally make small rice balls or sushi for them to eat before breakfast is ready.

If a child wakes up many times during the night, try to discover the reason. The problem may be due to something that was eaten at dinner such as bread, fruit, beans, or other foods that are difficult to digest. The same is true with dreams or nightmares. Parents need to understand how different foods create different effects on the child's mind and thinking. In this way they can come to understand how foods produce dreams. Some foods can cause children to have happy dreams while others produce unhappy ones.

Bathing—We recommend that children be given a mild warm bath everyday. The best time for children to bathe is in the evening just before bedtime, but not immediately after the evening meal. A bath directly following dinner may interfere with digestion. A bath just before bed can help the child relax and have a deep and peaceful sleep. If a family eats later in the evening, then children can have a bath before dinner is served. If daily bathing is done routinely and is a happy time for children, they will tend to develop regular bathing habits as they get older. Most children prefer to have a parent in the bathroom with them while they

are bathing, helping them to wash and enjoy their bath. A parent can supervise bathing until children are about five to six years old. Of course, children under three need constant watching and if an adult does leave the room for a few moments, make sure that there is very little water in the tub and that the parent does not go very far away. Older children enjoy bathing by themselves, especially when they reach the age of nine or so. If an older child wishes to bathe without anyone present, including younger brothers or sisters, it is better to respect their wishes.

Washing Up—When babies and young children wake up in the morning, parents can make it a practice of quickly washing their faces and hands. If this habit is established early on, children will usually continue it throughout life. Washing up before meals is also very important and can be taught to children at an early age.

Cleaning Teeth—Cleaning the teeth can begin as early as one-and-a-half to two. Parents can begin teaching children about cleaning their teeth even before that by letting them observe family members doing so. It is a good idea to purchase a small children's toothbrush and keep it on hand for the younger child to use as soon as he or she begins to show interest. Parents can show children how to properly clean the teeth and encourage them to do so regularly, so that by the age of five or six they enjoy doing it by themselves everyday.

Washing, bathing, and cleaning the teeth can be made fun and enjoyable. If parents request children to do these things in a demanding or unrelaxed way, children may develop a dislike or disinterest in these activities. Nagging never accomplishes anything except frustration and upset. Teaching good habits to older children is much more difficult, so it is important to begin daily hygiene while children are still young. If parents have regular bathing and cleaning habits the child will tend to imitate and develop them also.

Grooming Habits—Grooming habits can be encouraged at an early age. When children are young, games can be played to encourage the child to enjoy these activities. Singing songs or counting fingers and toes while trimming nails can help focus a child's interest and make him feel more relaxed. It is important to begin regular grooming habits when children are young so that they will continue as they grow older. Washing and combing young children's hair has to be done gently and peacefully. Children may develop a dislike or even fear of hair-washing or combing if they get soap in their eyes or if hair is pulled while combing.

Dressing and Undressing—As we have mentioned, the best children's clothing is made of high quality cotton fabric. Cotton keeps a child cool in the summer and warm in the winter. It is the ideal vegetable or natural quality fabric for clothing. Cotton is also easy to clean and lasts longer than synthetic fabrics. It is also very smooth and comfortable to wear. In the winter, woolen jackets, sweaters, mittens and hats can be worn on top of cotton clothing.

It is better if clothing is loose-fitting and comfortable, and allows a child freedom of movement. It is more difficult for children to relax and play in tight, restrictive clothing. Tight clothing can make a child uncomfortable and irritable.

The quality of shoes is also very important. Soft cotton or canvas sneakers are comfortable and practical. Children's feet grow very quickly. Parents need to pay careful attention to this, making sure that as a child's feet grow his or her shoes are comfortable. It is very difficult for children to relax if their shoes do not fit properly. Shoes that are too big can also cause problems, as a child may trip and fall easily, and may not be able to run, jump, and play with total freedom.[3]

As we have already said, high quality cotton pajamas are best. Synthetics often hold too much body heat and make children uncomfortable. Pajamas with feet attached also tend to keep the body too warm during sleep. Some children experience difficulty breathing properly when they wear pajamas of this type. Pajamas with attached feet often have plastic soles which are also not recommended. If a child's cotton pajamas have attached feet, simply cut the feet off to make them more comfortable for your child to sleep in. When pajamas are comfortable and loose fitting, a child can enjoy freedom of motion and can sleep soundly. In the morning, children can remove their underwear and pajamas and put on fresh clean underwear and clothing.

If children always have clean and neat clothing when they are young, and if parents teach the importance of dressing properly, children will tend to develop orderly habits of dress. If the proper care of clothing is neglected, it is much more difficult to encourage older children to dress well and to properly care for their clothes.

Learning to Walk

It is best if children learn to walk without much parental involvement. Do not attempt to force them to walk before they want to. Children should really try to do this themselves. Parental involvement should focus on making sure children are safe and not in danger of hurting themselves. Just be there to supervise and guide them when they need it. Some children walk very early, as young as ten to eleven months old, while others do not walk until they are two. Do not worry if another child is walking before yours. Each child is unique and his or her rate of growth and development should be respected. Wait until the child is stronger, more confident and interested in walking. If a child is being fed high quality food

[3] *Rice Straw Sandals:* When I was a young girl living in the countryside of Japan, I wore rice straw sandals. They were very comfortable and inexpensive. Sometimes my friends and I would go for long walks or picnics wearing one pair of these sandals and carrying another in a knapsack with our rice balls. If we were running and playing and one of our sandals broke, we just left them on the ground to decay and return to the soil, and would wear the extra pair in our knapsack to go back home. If both pairs broke, we could always buy another pair for just a few cents, as many farm houses had these sandals hanging up outside to sell to people walking by. It was so convenient and comfortable, and we never had to worry about shoes.—*Aveline Kushi.*

everyday, do not worry, he will walk when he is ready. Occasionally, children can be placed in a walker or a set that bounces to help them strengthen their leg muscles. Be careful, however, not to leave children in these devices for extended periods as it may cause them to become very tired and it may hurt the child's back to sit or stand for too long a time. Do not take drastic measures to force a child to walk. Using daily foods to make a child strong enough to begin walking is the best method.

Bowed legs and knock-knees are caused by imbalances in the diet. Bowed legs are often caused by overeating. Too much salt in the diet can increase a child's appetite and overeating results to balance this. If a child has this condition, extraordinary measures are usually unnecessary. Simply make adjustments in the child's food and in how it is prepared, and the condition will tend to correct itself. If a child's feet point inward, the cause is usually too much yin food. If they point outward, the cause is too much animal food. Simple changes in diet can help these conditions return to normal.

Using Spoons, Chopsticks, and Other Implements

Parents can actively teach children to use spoons and chopsticks properly when eating. Gently try to discourage them from eating with their fingers by showing them how to use a spoon or chopsticks. It is better for young children not to use a fork as it can be dangerous. If a child is using chopsticks, parents need to carefully supervise. Do not leave a child unattended while he or she is using chopsticks. Do not allow children to walk or run holding chopsticks (or any pointed object). If they fall, they could seriously injure themselves. It is the responsibility of parents to teach children to eat properly and safely. If children are left to themselves, they

will often eat with their fingers, often wasting food, creating a mess, and developing habits that will be difficult to break later on. Children who eat with their fingers may continue to do so even when they are older. This can be embarrassing and frustrating for both parents and child.

As children gain increasing fine muscle control, they naturally become interested in using crayons, pencils, pens, and paint brushes. Parents can guide children in how to hold these objects so they can draw or paint, or how to make the appropriate lines or strokes when they learn to write. Leave the creation of drawings and paintings to the child's imagination. If the child requests help or asks a parent to make a drawing, there is no harm in complying, but it is better not to interfere with what the child is creating. Let children initiate and create their own style. Young children can be encouraged to use crayons or chalk as they are safe. Pencils and pens can be given to older children or to younger children if properly supervised.

After a child finishes a drawing, discuss what it is that he or she has drawn and what the drawing means. It is best for adults not to tell children what they think a drawing represents. Rather encourage them to offer their own explanations.

The materials that a child uses for drawing, painting, or play should be safe, non-toxic and more natural in quality. Provide children with clay, paper, paints, and crayons to play with rather than plastic or synthetic materials. Cutting out paper drawings with safe children's scissors is also a very good activity. Try to encourage children to play and develop their creativity rather than pursuing more passive activities like watching television. Television has a strong influence on how children behave so when they do watch it, make sure that the program is suitable.

Encourage children to invent their own play and games. If children have too many toys they may become frustrated and confused. They may not play with their toys or may have difficulty deciding how to go about playing with them. Having fewer toys can make things simpler for a child. When children are very young, even when they start to crawl, let them help pick up and put away their toys. If they are taught how to do this at an early age, most children will develop orderly habits and will clean up after themselves when they play. If children do not learn this when they are young, it may be difficult for them to change later. Children can also be shown how to wash their dishes after meals around the age of two.

When children are eleven to twelve years old, or even younger, parents can begin teaching them how to sew, knit, wash clothes, iron, wash dishes, and fold and put away clothing. They can also be involved in doing chores around the house and in helping with younger children by reading and playing with them.

Teaching children to cook when they are young is very valuable training. However, it is better to wait to teach them how to cut vegetables until they are older, as their coordination is usually not well enough developed to handle a knife properly. Once children are taught how to use a knife they will often try to do it without supervision and this could be dangerous. Put cutting knives out of the reach of younger children. It is difficult to constantly watch a child when trying

to cook and care for other children. It is better to wait until children are eight or nine before teaching them to cut vegetables. Younger children can learn how to make things that are safer and easier and do not require using a sharp knife.

Daily Interaction with Others

The foods that parents prepare and serve to their children daily are the most important factors in determining how they interact with other children and adults. The actions and behavior of parents and other adults also influence children, but the key factor is daily food. Children who eat well generally develop a good-natured, peaceful disposition and enjoy interacting with other children and adults. Watch what children eat and observe how different foods affect their behavior. Through careful observation parents will learn how to adjust their cooking to help them. It is a good idea not to habitually tell children how they should and should not behave. When they eat something and do not feel well or if they do not get along with others, do not scold children or make them feel bad. Talk with them and try to get them to see how certain foods affect them. Show children how they can change. Teach them at an early age to notice how food affects their behavior and health.

Try to teach, encourage, and inspire children rather than dominating or controlling them. In this way, they will be happy.

Teething

Some children get their first teeth at four months, but as a general rule, the first teeth come in at about the age of six to eight months. Some babies may not get teeth until later. Do not worry about this. All babies are different and develop at different rates. If parents are eating well and feeding their baby good food, he or she will probably not have much trouble when teeth do come in. It is only when the cooking is out of balance—creating an overly yin or yang condition in the baby—that teething problems arise.

If the baby wants something to chew on, she can be given a large piece or section of raw carrot. Make sure that it is big enough to hold on to and too large to choke on. When a baby is given a piece of raw carrot, supervise closely to make sure that none of it is bitten off. High quality wooden rattles for babies to chew on can be also purchased. Also, hard teething biscuits can be made with whole wheat pastry flour. Shape the flour into thick cookies with interesting shapes. Bake them slowly with a low flame until they are very hard and do not break. Do not use salt or oil when making them. Parents can also massage the gums occasionally with their finger or let the baby chew on their finger.

When the permanent teeth begin to come in, be very careful to offer children a well-balanced diet to help them keep their teeth in good condition. Cavities can be caused by extremes of yin or yang, including sweets such as grain candy, cookies, juice, and concentrated sweeteners; as well as from salty foods or condiments. Be careful not to give children too many of these items.

When teeth protrude outward the cause is too much yin (fruit, juice, concentrated sweeteners, etc.) while teeth that point inward are caused by more yang types of foods, especially fish and salty dishes or condiments. Gray spots on the teeth are caused by too much salt. Discolored teeth can be caused by either extreme. Soft teeth are often caused by a lack of minerals or by the intake of too much yin food.

It is much easier to prevent problems with the teeth by giving children a naturally balanced diet than it is to correct them once they have developed.

Toilet Training

Toilet training takes time and patience on the part of parents. Several weeks of concentrated effort may be required. The earlier toilet training is started, the better, because it is easier at an earlier age. Children who are trained earlier usually require less time to learn to go to the toilet by themselves. Children will usually not train themselves, although there are some exceptions. Parents really need to make an effort to guide them properly. There is a trainer in Japan who teaches parents how to begin training their babies at the age of one to three months. Training this early can be done more easily if parents set up a regular time to place the child on the potty seat. Also, younger children often give signals when they are ready to have a bowel movement. Babies often prepare for a bowel movement by puckering their lips tightly and making their expression look more serious. They may also make certain noises that parents can come to recognize. When children are about to urinate, they sometimes make little noises or become a little fussy. If parents have the time to begin training a baby at a young age it will be much easier for both them and the child.

When babies are still in diapers and have not yet been trained, it is important to always make sure that their diapers are clean. Leaving soiled or wet diapers on a child is very uncomfortable and annoying. Babies may develop a rash if their diapers are not changed regularly or if they are not properly cleaned after changing. These practices are very important in helping children learn good bathroom and cleanliness habits.

Play and Movement

For enjoyment, creativity and happiness, it is very important for children to be physically and mentally active. Encourage children to participate in a wide variety of activities. Sports, gymnastics, dancing, painting, drawing, playing piano or other instruments, and pottery and other artistic classes are only a few of the activities children can participate in. Encourage them to have a wide variety of friends to broaden their social experience. Children are usually much happier if they are busily involved with many activities and social experiences.

More about Toys

It is better to select high quality handcrafted toys or toys made from more natural materials rather than mass-produced or electric toys. If a child's first toys are of a more natural quality she will often enjoy and be satisfied with them. But if plastic or electric toys are bought first, there may be some difficulty switching an older child over to more simple wooden toys. Children can be much more creative with more simple, natural toys that require energy and imagination. The vibration of wooden toys is peaceful and not upsetting. Electric or battery-operated toys can sometimes be frustrating for children to play with. Plastic toys tend to break easily, causing a child to become upset, whereas wooden toys are usually stronger and last for many years. Sturdier wooden toys can be handed down from child to child. In the long run, they are more economical and certainly more ecological than disposable plastic items.

Playing Outside

Playing outside in all seasons is very important for a child's physical and mental health and well-being. It is much easier for children to play outside if their home is in the country. For children who live in cities, parents may have to devote a little more time with them at the park or playground. It is helpful for children's social development if they can go to a park or playground everyday to play with other children. Children who spend a great deal of time outdoors are usually happier, and eat and sleep better than children who spend much time indoors. Children need open spaces to run, jump, play, and feel free in with little adult interference. Parents can, of course, accompany children on outings to look after their safety. They can also join in the play when children request it, or to help children get started.

It is also important for parents to periodically stop to point out different flowers and trees, and marvel out loud at the beauty of our natural world. Look up at the sky and ask children if they find it wonderful and beautiful to look at. Point out different clouds, birds, and animals. Try to instill in them a deep wonder and appreciation for nature. If children develop love and respect for nature, they will treat it with care and respect when they become adults.

It is important to take children to a variety of places such as the beach, zoo,

parks, farms, and forest, instead of visiting the same place day after day. Taking children to many different places will stimulate their creativity, imagination, and desire to learn. They will have the opportunity to observe many types of people and social situations.

Developing physical strength is very important for a child's health and confidence. Encourage children to participate in as many sports and game activities as possible. Children who are physically strong are often more happy, healthy, and confident. If a child is more physically weak, encouraging him to participate in sports activities can help him overcome this problem.

Balancing Play and Study

In planning a child's day, allow time for active play and more quiet activities, such as looking at picture books, drawing, or study. Parents can set aside time each day for toddlers to learn how to make things or to read or study together. If children develop these habits when they are young, they will usually continue into adulthood. When children start school, it is important that they have time to sit quietly and read or do their homework. School children need a clean, quiet, and orderly space for studying and doing homework. It is better for them to finish their homework before watching television. If they stay up late watching television—promising to do their homework afterward—they may become too tired to do it.

If children are not interested in studying or in doing homework, or are too active to sit quietly, simple dietary changes can usually help them calm down. A nice warm bath will often help a child relax.

Parents can stimulate a child's interest in study by making it fun and interesting. Usually, if parents participate actively in encouraging and occasionally helping children with their studies, children will take much more interest and pride in what they do. Also, if children frequently observe their parents studying and reading, they will usually try to imitate them. It is better not to nag children about doing homework. Help them set up a quiet time each day for their studies. When necessary, parents can adjust their schedule to spend time with a child to help with homework. It is better if children do their homework in a relaxed, enjoyable atmosphere. If there are younger children in the family, see to it that they are in bed or occupied in some way so as not to disturb the older child while he or she is studying.

Social Play

It is very important for children to be socially active even at an early age. Parents can encourage sociability by taking children to parks and other places to meet and play with other children. Open up the home to children's friends. Encourage

children to invite their friends home to play and encourage children to visit their friends' homes as well. This can help children learn how other people live, how to cooperate and play happily in an orderly manner, and how to share with friends. It is very good for children to have a wide variety of friends, so that they can learn to communicate with a variety of people, and be flexible under many different circumstances.

Parties, birthday parties, social events, play groups, sports, school activities, and after-school programs are also recommended to help children develop social awareness.

Special Notes for Parents

When a Baby Arrives—Once a child is born, he or she naturally becomes the center of the family. If the parents are eating well and have a balanced condition, there should be very little problem adjusting to the new baby. It will happen quite naturally. Of course, with the birth of a child, parents do need to make some changes in their daily lives. If a mother is eating well, the quality of her breast milk will most likely cause her baby to be very peaceful, to sleep well, and in general, to be healthy and content. When this is the case, parents have the freedom to go out socially with their new baby and can have their privacy as well. If a mother is not eating a balanced diet—for example, eating too many sweets or using too much salt—problems may develop with her breast milk and her baby may not enjoy a balanced condition. It is very important for a mother to eat well during the time that she breast-feeds, both for the health of her child and to make her and her husband's adjustment as smooth as possible. Of course, once a baby arrives, parents will most likely adjust their social activities to those which they

can easily handle with the baby present and those which are most peaceful for the baby as well.

Helping Older Children Adjust to a New Baby—Before a new baby arrives, it is best to prepare older children by talking with them about the baby. Parents can invite them to go shopping for baby clothing and accessories. But be careful not to talk too much about the coming baby, as children may become jealous. When the baby arrives, try not to focus attention exclusively on the baby when older children are present. Sometimes older children may think that parents like the baby more than them if parents are always talking about the new baby. Try to give older children a little extra attention to reassure them that they are still loved. Involve older children in helping bathe the baby, changing diapers, and other simple routines. The arrival of a new baby can be difficult, especially for children under five. Parents need to be understanding, patient, and loving at this time.

Single Parents—As we saw in Chapter One, the number of single parent families is increasing. Some families are single parent families from the beginning, while others come about as the result of divorce, separation or the death of one of the partners. At present, it is estimated that one in three American families are single parent families. (In Great Britain, the rate is approximately one in four; in Australia, one in six.) In about 90 percent of these cases, the father is the absent parent.

It is difficult for the single parent to play the role of both parents. One way to help compensate is to make opportunities for the child to associate with others, for example at parks, playgrounds, parties, and other social events. Visiting with friends and their families will also help a child adjust to having one parent. If children are socially active and do things together with their parents they will be happier and adjust more smoothly.

Avoiding Accidents—A balanced natural diet, strong, clear cooking, and a little common sense are primary in preventing accidents. When a child's food is balanced, his or her coordination, intuition, and judgment function more efficiently. Accidents are much less likely when the child has a more balanced condition. Parents need to continually observe their children's diet and condition so as to correct any imbalances.

Common sense precautions in regard to potential hazards are of course necessary. When babies gain the ability to roll over, they must be continually watched and not left unsupervised on tables or other places that they could fall from. When children start to crawl or walk, parents need to watch potential problem areas such as stairs, electrical outlets, and kitchen cabinets. When children climb on furniture, parents must of course keep a close watch. Potentially hazardous objects—including kitchen utensils and matches, and potentially dangerous substances—need to be kept safely away from children. It is best never to leave young children without proper adult supervision. They also require careful attention when playing outside.

Parents' health, judgment and good sense are, obviously, essential in maintaining the health and well-being of children. Young children depend entirely upon the good judgment of their parents for their health and safety. Proper eating, an orderly, natural lifestyle, and a loving concern for the welfare of children can help in preventing most problems. Parents must also teach children about safety—including how to properly cross streets and how to relate to strangers—as soon as they begin to explore the world around them.

When children reach the age at which they start to go outside by themselves, parents can establish the routine of having children always tell them where they are going and what they will be doing. Parents can ask children to call when they arrive, and to let them know when and how they plan to return home. It is important to keep aware of what children are doing and where they are going. When children return home, ask them what they were doing and whether or not they enjoyed themselves. Always keep the lines of communication open and friendly.

Parental Guidance—Approaches to the question of parental guidance can be divided into two general categories. The more yang approach is *authoritarian*. It often involves rigid rules or attitudes that parents wish to impose upon children. It frequently employs punishment if children break these rules or fail to do what parents expect. In extreme cases, parents may believe that children are inherently bad and must be reformed, with physical punishment if necessary.

The more yin approach to discipline can be referred to as *permissiveness*. In recent times, it has developed largely as a counterbalance to the perceived harshness of the authoritarian approach. In extreme instances, parents allow children to do almost anything they wish in the belief that any type of restraint could be harmful to the child's development.

It is important to remember that each child is a manifestation of the infinite universe, or God. Children are by nature no more "bad" than the sun, the stars, or any other natural phenomenon. On the contrary, if their natural tendencies and instincts are allowed to mature fully, all human beings seek universal love and harmony. What are usually thought of as negative aspects of human nature represent the incomplete development of humanity's natural tendencies. It is important therefore to unconditionally love all children and to respect their integrity as a manifestation of God.

In Chapter One, we saw how imbalances in daily diet and environment can lead to the abnormal psychological conditions that produce child abuse. Striking or punishing a child out of anger, devising some form of calculated punishment, or ignoring a child's safety are indications of physical and mental imbalance. An overly rigid or authoritarian approach to children often develops when the consumption of meat, eggs, fish, poultry or other yang quality foods—including salt and minerals—becomes excessive. An excessively permissive approach develops more easily with the excessive intake of refined or chemicallized foods, tropical fruits, sugar, chocolate, milk, ice cream and other more yin items.

For example, hitting children is usually the result of anger or frustration on the part of parents. Psychologists have discovered that children who are hit usually do not remember what they were punished for and do not change their behavior as a result. Children who are hit rarely feel sorry for their actions, and striking children tends to establish a pattern of physical abuse in the household. Children who are hit often begin to hit their younger brothers and sisters, and grow up with the belief that violence toward other human beings is an acceptable method for solving problems.

It is up to the parents to educate and guide children toward a proper way of life. When children behave in an unhealthy or abnormal way, parents should realize that they themselves are the major cause, either through providing children with excessive or unbalanced food or through the example of their own daily behavior.

In a more balanced approach, harmony is the underlying principle of relations between husband and wife and parents and children. Harmony is either maintained or disrupted primarily by the quality of food prepared daily. The question of how children behave cannot be separated from the overall health and way of living of the family as a whole. A more balanced approach is neither authoritarian or permissive to the extent that no constructive guidance is provided. It is based on a keen observation of how children are behaving and an understanding of the underlying causes of their behavior. When behavior becomes out of balance or one-sided, parents can lovingly help their children reestablish equilibrium.

When children develop a problem with behavior, discuss it with them and try to find out the cause. It may be something they are eating or may be due to inattention from you, the parents. When talking with them, let children see how their behavior may not be in their best interests or in the interest of family harmony. If children consistently repeat their mistakes without learning from them, a more firm approach may be necessary. However, always remember that food and the environment in the home are the underlying cause of most problems, and that behavior itself is basically the reflection of the quality of these factors.

Teaching Children to Care for Their Health—Parents will want to begin when children are very small to teach them how to take care of their health. Show them how to chew properly. If they have a stomachache, explain to them that instead of eating heavy foods at that time, a simpler meal will make them feel much better. Make sure to check their bowel movement everyday when they are very young. When they become older, parents can ask children to let them know whenever they have a problem with their bowel movement, for example, if it becomes too dark, or if they develop diarrhea or constipation. There is no need to discuss their bowel condition everyday, but if it becomes abnormal, it is important for children to tell parents right away. If we explain to them why this is important, they will not feel embarrassed to discuss it. If older children wet the bed often, it is also a sign that their condition is becoming out of balance. It is important to discuss problems such as these and to cooperate with children in making the appropriate changes in their daily food so as to correct imbalances before they become serious.

Teaching children how to make balance is an essential tool for their future health and happiness. Begin by explaining foods in terms of yin and yang. Tell them, for example, that animal products, such as meat, poultry, and eggs are very yang. Explain that sugar, honey, tropical fruits, spices, soft drinks, chocolate, and candy are very yin. Tell them that these foods are generally too extreme for use in maintaining health, and that more centrally balanced foods like whole grains, beans, and fresh local vegetables are best for maintaining a healthy condition.

If children develop some type of symptom such as a runny nose or sneezing, ask them what they ate in order to help them see the connection between their eating and day-to-day condition. Parents can also explain their condition in terms of yin and yang, for example by telling them that a runny nose or sneezing is often caused by too many more yin foods and drinks.

When explaining things in yin and yang terms, it is better to avoid using words like "good" and "bad." Yin and yang are simply complementary yet antagonistic tendencies that are found throughout nature. Thinking in terms of "right" and "wrong" can lead to a one-sided view of life.

Parents can show their children how yin and yang apply to all areas of life. Adults should try to express themselves simply and poetically in language that children can understand. Yin and yang can also be taught by pointing out the spiral pattern in nature. Draw children's attention to the many spirals that exist in nature, from galaxies to the spiral on the top of the head. (Please refer to Aveline Kushi's book for children, *Lessons of Night and Day*, for ideas on how to express yin and yang in a simple, colorful and poetic manner.)

As we have already said, habits of cleanliness and good grooming can be taught at an early age. Children can also be encouraged to clean their room, make their bed, and in general, to participate in household chores.

Applying Home Care—In the following chapter, we discuss the macrobiotic approach to common childhood illnesses. In some cases, we recommend simple home care applications, including light massage, compresses, and palm healing. Below are general comments on how to apply home care for children.

For generations, traditional families employed a variety of simple methods for home health care. Basic *shiatsu,* or finger pressure massage, simple compresses made from items used everyday in the kitchen, and special dishes and beverages were used commonly in the home. Mild shiatsu, for example, can be given to children (or adults, including senior citizens) to help relax and harmonize their overall condition. In traditional families, husbands and wives would frequently exchange shiatsu massage, and would periodically offer a simple treatment to their children or elderly parents as well.

We recommend that all members of a family learn basic healing arts as a part of home health care.

Palm healing is usually not a problem for children because it makes them calm and relaxed. Just be careful to apply your hands very lightly and make sure that the child is kept properly covered and warm during an application. If a child falls asleep during palm healing, the application may be continued until it is complete. Simply tuck the child in after it is finished.

When compresses and other home applications are used, make sure that they are very mild in comparison to those used by adults. Adjust the application to fit each child's needs. This may seem like a very small thing but it is very important. If parents are inexperienced in using macrobiotic applications, it is best not to do anything drastic or strong. It is also a good idea to call a macrobiotic center. Examine the child's bowel movement everyday; if he or she is constipated, a simple enema can be given after two or three days. Many simple problems start in the intestines. When children have fever, it is usually better to give them milder applications, such as putting green cabbage leaves on the forehead. If an application that is too strong is given, it may cause a reaction and the child may take longer to recover.

It is also not necessary to give extreme or unusual tasting medicinal foods or drinks to children. For instance, if a child has a fever, we usually recommend warm apple juice or mildly roasted grain tea. But for an adult we usually recommend fresh grated daikon tea. Daikon tea is too strong for young children and they usually do not like to drink it. Sweeter or more mild tasting drinks are more appropriate for children. When children are sick, it is often necessary to adjust their surroundings to keep them comfortable, for example, by seeing that their room is warm or by using steam to keep the air moist. The atmosphere in the home is very important at all times, and especially when a child is not feeling well.

It is important for parents to remain calm and positive when children become sick. Children are very sensitive to their parents' emotions, and may become frightened or upset if the parents are tense.

Many books recommend placing a child in a cold bath when a fever develops. However, this may cause an extreme reaction, such as a seizure. In the past, parents would keep children with fevers warm and not let their skin get cold. When children are kept warm they naturally perspire, and this cools the body. If parents place children in a cool bath, apply cold towels or give a cold water sponge bath, the surface of their skin will contract and become tight. When this happens the discharge of a fever goes deeper into the body instead of coming out. This can be especially dangerous in cases of measles.

If problems arise, watch the child's diet and find out what he or she has been eating. This will help decide what steps to take. If a child's diet is balanced, and if his mother ate well while she was pregnant and breast-feeding, the problems that arise are usually less extreme and easier to correct. Children who eat well sometimes intuitively know what they need to correct a problem and may refuse remedies that are too extreme. Parents should observe and learn from their children's responses.

A Word to Grandparents—It is important for grandparents to cooperate with their children when it comes to grandchildren. It often happens that grandparents and

parents have different ideas on child-raising. If so, the issues should be discussed openly in order to reach a suitable agreement and to avoid arguments or misunderstandings. In this way parents and grandparents relate to the children in a similar manner. This is also much better for the children. It is less confusing and makes for better communication between children, parents, and grandparents. Grandparents need to respect their children's ideas on how to raise their children. Remember that the parents are the ones who are responsible for their children twenty-four hours a day, whereas grandparents can enjoy a much easier and relaxed relationship with their grandchildren. At the same time, grandparents possess a wealth of experience in child rearing. Parents are fortunate if they can turn to their own parents for advice and suggestions.

Chapter 4

Keeping Children Healthy

Children come to this earth from the infinite universe, and childhood is a stage in their return journey to infinity. Health and peace, joy and adventure, and wonder and marvel are all natural states for children. They exist when children live in harmony with the laws of nature. But what is health?

Health is much more than freedom from illness. It includes continual growth, flexible change, and joyful adaptation to the ever changing world. It is the natural outcome of a way of life in harmony with the cycles of nature. When children are healthy, they enjoy the following attributes:

1. *Boundless energy, creativity, and enthusiasm.* Healthy children play from morning to evening without growing bored or exhausted. Little ones may of course require a nap from time to time, but when they are awake, they are active and full of energy; so much so, in fact, that parents often have trouble keeping up with them. A good way to evaluate our own health is to consider how well we keep pace with our children.

   A healthy child will approach life with a spirit of adventure. The energetic pursuit of dreams and ambitions, including the capacity to play, make-

believe, fantasize, and daydream, is a sign of good health and sound development. These capacities foster children's development, and help them realize their dreams throughout life.

2. *A good appetite.* Children normally have healthy appetites, and not simply for food. A good appetite includes the desire for love, friendship, adventure, knowledge, and new experiences.

Children are born with an unlimited curiosity. This is reflected, as they grow, by their love of riddles, games, puzzles, and things that need to be figured out. They are always asking questions, and have a tremendous desire to participate in life.

Children also seek love and friendship. They have no trouble making friends with children of their own age, with adults, or even with younger children or babies. Through their rich imaginations, they can also become friends with toys, animals, trees, rocks, and almost anything else they come into contact with. The ability to make friends easily is a sign that a child is healthy and well adjusted.

Too much rich food or too many luxuries can spoil a child's appetite. For example, children are naturally attracted to sweet-tasting foods. However, if they indulge in sugary snacks, soda, candy, ice cream, or other poor quality foods, they will spoil their health. It is important for parents to use good judgment when selecting their children's snacks and sweets. At the same time, children need opportunities to solve problems and confront challenges. This helps them to develop endurance, vitality, and patience. They will then be better equipped to deal with the challenges that arise during their lives.

It is an expression of parental love to encourage moderation. When children are old enough, explain to them that overindulgence can lead to dullness, stagnation, and weakness. Help them to understand that moderation actually strengthens and enhances their ability to participate in life. Moderation is not punishment; it is a means to further self growth and development.

3. *Deep, sound sleep.*   When children are healthy, they enjoy good, sound sleep. Energetic physical and mental activity produces deep and restful sleep. When a healthy child sleeps, he or she is not bothered by nightmares or rootless, disturbing dreams. These come from imbalances in the brain and nervous system that result from excesses in the daily diet and environment. Television, movies, and other types of mental stimulation can also interact with a poor quality diet to produce disturbing and frightening dreams.

4. *Good memory and imagination.*   Good memory is a sign of health. Memory provides the basis for all learning. Learning to walk, to control bowel movements and urination, to speak, read, write, and do arithmetic all rest on the foundation of memory. Children learn to remember letters, numbers, and words, and to recreate scenery, people, and events, as well as emotions and feelings. They also have an intuitive memory of their spiritual origins. Imagination, creativity, ambition, and future plans or dreams are all based on memory. Memory is the foundation of health and happiness.

The ease with which children make friends is a result of their universal memory. Children intuitively remember their origin in the infinite universe, and realize instinctively that all people and things share the same origin. More relative or artificial distinctions such as race, occupation, nationality or religious belief are usually not important to children and do not interfere with the desire to make friends. Children are naturally citizens of one world.

5. *Freedom from anger, fear, and other negative emotions.*   As we saw in the first chapter, negative emotions correlate to physical disorders. In Oriental countries, for example, anger was described as "pain in the liver." Stagnation and other liver troubles frequently result from eating too many animal foods, baked or overly cooked dishes, and mineral salts. Foods such as these can interfere with the natural flow of earth's energy up the right side of the body. In this case, energy becomes stagnant and accumulates in the liver. Then, like a volcano, this stagnated energy periodically explodes in an outburst that we call anger. Children who are naturally healthy do not have this stagnation and thus rarely experience anger.

Fear is related to an imbalance in the kidneys, often as a result of the overintake of fluids, saturated fats, sugar, animal proteins, and mineral salts. The kidneys stabilize the flow of energy in the body by harmonizing the energy that flows up through the right and down the left side of the body. When this balancing function is disturbed, a person loses confidence and stability.

The tendency toward fear is of course reinforced when parents strike or punish children, or when children experience artificial or painful procedures such as injections, operations, x-rays, and so on. Teachers or other adults can instill fear when they assume an overly authoritarian or disciplinarian posture. Fear of nuclear war, or failure to measure up to expectations, and fear of the future in general are becoming common among children today. Underlying imbalances in diet promote fear rather than a positive confidence in the future based on the desire to meet and overcome these challenges.

Abnormal mental or emotional conditions relate directly to imbalances in diet and upbringing. These imbalances distort the normal patterns of energy flow through the major organs and the body as a whole. As a result, these disruptions can prevent more healthy emotional and intellectual responses.

The perception that physical health affects the emotions is not new. Traditional societies around the world have recognized the link between an individual's physical health and his or her emotional expression. Various cultures, in fact, have discussed this connection in a highly detailed way.

Today, researchers are finding that there indeed appears to be a relationship between mind and body. In the future, we can expect growing scientific recognition of this fact, and the application of this relationship to solve a wide variety of problems.

In the following chart we present common psychological problems and correlate them with the major organs of the body. The dietary and psychological imbalances that promote these tendencies are also presented.

The underlying physical correlations that are associated with these psychological disturbances are preventable through proper diet. A centrally balanced diet—with an ample variety of wholesome foods and styles of cooking—can help the body maintain the proper flow of energy. The organs and systems then function smoothly and efficiently, creating physical and emotional well-being. In cases where problems already exist, a balanced diet can help in the recovery of more harmonious psychological and emotional states.

At the same time, changing the psychological factors that contribute to the particular problem will accelerate recovery. For example, a child who is continually put under pressure to behave properly or to perform according to certain expectations can easily become frustrated or angry, especially when he or she eats plenty of animal protein and fat. Parents can help change this situation by treating the child in a more relaxed and supporting manner, while of course adjusting the child's diet. Parents may also begin to show more of an interest in the things the child is doing, and actively support whatever he or she is engaged in.

Table 7

Psychological Symptoms	Related Organ Dysfunction	Contributing Psychological Factors	Contributing Dietary Imbalances
Anger—including argumentative, explosive, or abusive behavior; frequent complaining; hitting or punishing others; bullying	Liver and gallbladder	Too much external control or pressure; lack of recognition, appreciation, or encouragement	The overconsumption of more extremely yang foods including meat, eggs, poultry and cheese; too many baked flour products or salt; and a lack of freshness in the diet; i.e., foods that interfere with the smooth upward flow of energy
Excitement—including nervousness; frequently changing one's mind; overly emotional behavior	Heart and small intestine	Lack of discipline; spoiling children, overly sentimental parental care	Excessive yin and yang combined, including animal foods, sugar, hot spicy foods and tropical fruits; too many raw foods
Doubt—including suspicion; lack of warmth; or an overly critical attitude	Spleen, pancreas and stomach	An undependable environment	Excessive yin foods and beverages, including milk, ice cream, butter, soft drinks, sugar, tropical fruits, and spices
Mental rigidity—including stubbornness; narrow- or closed-mindedness; or rejecting others' advice or opinions	Lungs and large intestine	Loneliness; lack of warmth; a cold, uncaring environment	Heavy, fatty foods; foods with a sticky quality; baked foods; salt
Fear—including insecurity; anxiety; overprotectiveness	Kidneys and bladder	An overly protective environment; parents often critical of others	Excessive yin and yang combined, especially saltier or more heavily cooked dishes; extreme yin including drugs

Children who frequently become overexcited, nervous, or hysterical often improve when provided with situations that challenge their abilities to a reasonable degree. Solving problems and overcoming difficulties helps them to become stronger and more self-controlled. Spoiling children who manifest this problem only serves to reinforce their behavior. Encouraging self-discipline can help the child recover a healthy equilibrium. Keeping a calm and relaxed atmosphere at home will of course help the child become more peaceful.

Doubt and suspicion can be offset by providing children with a stable and dependable environment. Keeping promises and establishing dependable routines in daily life contribute to the establishment of faith and trust.

The tendency toward mental rigidity, stubbornness, or narrow-mindedness can be offset by providing a warm, loving, and supportive home environment. Mental rigidity and stubbornness can cause an individual to become isolated from others. Therefore, it is important for parents to get involved in their children's activities and offer them frequent companionship in order to offset loneliness and isolation.

Fear or anxiety can be offset by reassuring children about their bright future and allowing them freedom to experience things for themselves. Being overly protective can often increase anxiety, especially later when children are alone and must confront difficulties by themselves. Parents can also minimize this tendency by not speaking negatively about others and by frequently showing praise and admiration for others in front of their children.

6. *A joyful response to the environment.* Healthy children respond joyfully to the changing world around them. They are able to respond in an original

and flexible way, without more set or predictable patterns of thought and behavior.

Open-mindedness is also a characteristic of healthy children. They can entertain new ideas and situations without prejudice or preconceived notions. Children are usually much more adaptable than adults—who tend to be more set in their ways. Children are also very resilient; they are able to spring back from illness, failure, or difficulty and resume their play and activities with rapid speed.

7. *Wonder, marvel, and appreciation.* Children find wonder everywhere. They intuitively sense a oneness with all things, and are grateful for their life on this earth as a human being. Their appreciation is often expressed simply in their joy of living, or in simple expressions of love and tenderness toward parents, brothers and sisters, and friends.

Understanding Sickness

The majority of sicknesses that affect normally healthy children are of the adjustment variety. *Adjustment sicknesses* arise when a normally healthy child eats some type of extreme or unbalanced food that sets off a discharge that may take the form of fever, coughing, runny nose, sore throat, or vomiting. Adjustments usually come on suddenly and pass as soon as the excess is discharged and the child returns to a more balanced condition.

Aside from simple adjustments in diet and home care, it is preferable not to interfere with the natural process of discharge unless the symptoms become severe. If a child eats well while the adjustment is going on, he or she can quickly return to normal and experience a strengthening of natural immunity and self-healing power.

Children also adjust to their environment by discharging factors that were taken in during the embryonic period. Measles, for example, represents the discharge of more yang factors taken in during the time in the womb. The discharge of these factors furthers normal growth and development.

Another type of discharge can occur from imbalances in the mother's diet during the period of breast-feeding. These may take the form of rashes, eye discharges, or a runny nose. As with other simple adjustments, the symptoms normally subside once the intake of excess is stopped and a more balanced diet adopted.

In some cases, however, a baby will discharge even when the nursing mother is eating well. These discharges can be the result of extremes taken in during pregnancy. In one case, a six-month-old baby developed a rash on his cheeks. The skin became dry, red and tight. His mother had been macrobiotic for several years and was eating well during the time that she was nursing. When the rash started, she was careful to limit her intake of oil, flour products, fish, fruit desserts, and other items that could produce discharge.

However, during pregnancy she went to a restaurant several times and ate a baked potato together with spaghetti and plain tomato sauce. The excessive factors in these foods were absorbed by the baby and discharged after birth. The hard dry skin on the baby's cheeks was similar to the skin of a baked potato. The tomato sauce came out in the form of the red inflammation. The rash continued for several months until these foods were discharged. During this time the mother ate well and applied a *nuka* (rice bran) skin wash to the inflamed cheeks. Now, several years later, the skin is completely normal and the child has had no further outbreaks of the rash.

Degenerative sicknesses are more serious. They result from the chronic deterioration of the body's organs and functions, and are more infrequent among children and young people than they are among adults and older people. These illnesses normally take longer to develop, and result from chronic imbalances in the daily diet and way of life. The degenerative process may not produce noticeable symptoms until many years have passed. However, even though they may not reach a critical stage until years later, degenerative processes frequently begin in childhood. Many children and young people have elevated cholesterol levels and hardening of the arteries, both of which lead to heart disease. Children also suffer from degenerative conditions such as epilepsy, asthma, cystic fibrosis, multiple sclerosis, diabetes, muscular dystrophy, and mental disturbances, as well as cancer and AIDS. Leukemia and other cancers have increased so that they are now the second leading cause of death among children under fifteen.

Another category of disorders occurs when an acute, severe adjustment leads to a rapid deterioration in the quality of the blood, cells, and organs. These *adjustment/degenerative* disorders occur when a chronically unbalanced diet creates an abnormal condition in the blood and body fluids, cells, and tissues. With this underlying condition as a base, adjustments can escalate into a more serious degenerative condition. Examples include meningitis resulting from improper handling of the measles, pneumonia, polio, rheumatic fever, smallpox, and sudden infant death syndrome (SIDS). An extreme or unbalanced diet weakens natural immunity and increases susceptibility to infectious disorders. Children with more healthy autoimmune systems enjoy natural immunity from many of the common infectious conditions encountered during childhood.

In general, simple adjustments involve a child's daily *condition*, especially blood quality, which is always changing in response to diet and environment. Degenerative sicknesses are much deeper. They affect the *constitution*, including the structure and quality of the organs and tissues. The constitution begins forming during pregnancy, and degenerative disorders frequently originate with the foods eaten during this period or even prior to conception when they affect the parents' reproductive cells. The wide range of birth defects, for example, result from extremes in the diet or environment during pregnancy or before conception.

An extreme diet during pregnancy can create constitutional weakness. These deficiencies are often the basis for the development of many of the degenerative conditions that appear in childhood or later in life. However, the macrobiotic diet and way of life strengthens the constitution and can prevent many degenerative conditions from developing. The constitution is not completely formed until maturity. It is influenced by the quality of foods eaten in childhood and during the period of growth. Many children who have started macrobiotics have experienced improvement in a variety of chronic conditions and an overall strengthening of their physical and mental vitality. Children who are macrobiotic from conception, or prior to conception, are often born with strong constitutions. If they continue to eat well, they can enjoy good health throughout their lives and remain free of more serious illness.

In the following sections we present the macrobiotic approach to common childhood problems. It is important to remember that these recommendations are for educational purposes and do not represent medical advice. They should not be used in place of qualified medical care. Emergency cases require prompt medical attention. At the same time, we suggest that you contact a qualified macrobiotic center or instructor when making changes in a child's diet or way of life, or when applying home care. Appropriate resources are now available throughout the world and we advise all parents to make use of them. Thousands of parents have used simple methods such as those that follow and have found them safe and effective in keeping their children healthy.

The following home recommendations are safe, simple to use, and can be very effective. However, it is far better to avoid imbalances on a day-to-day basis, or to deal with them as they develop, rather than trying to make adjustments after imbalances begin to cause troublesome symptoms.

Study, discussing questions and problems with friends, and experience will develop judgment and enable parents to be sensitive to the conditions of their children and other family members. Remember that a balanced diet and way of life are the factors that determine our physical and emotional well-being.

Simple Fever

When children eat a naturally balanced diet, they rarely experience fever. With the exception of measles—which represents a normal discharge—children who eat properly experience fever only when their diet or environment becomes extreme.

Simple fevers represent the discharge of excessive factors. Depending upon the type of excess being discharged, the fever may or may not be accompanied by other discharge symptoms such as coughing, runny nose, or sore throat.

In most cases, fevers are not serious and respond to simple home care. Fevers that indicate serious illness are usually accompanied by other symptoms, such as difficulty in breathing, extreme listlessness, or behavioral disturbance. Fevers that are more serious are usually those resulting from obvious medical emergencies such as heatstroke or poisoning. Parents suspecting an emergency condition are of course advised to seek appropriate medical attention.

Simple fevers result when the discharge of vibration from metabolic activity becomes excessive. This discharge may take many forms, one of which is heat. In Oriental medicine, the generation of heat from metabolic activity is coordinated by what is referred to as the body's *triple heater* function. The name triple heater comes from the three energy centers, or *chakras*, where this function is coordinated. The generation of heat in the upper body is centered around the heart energy center, or chakra; in the mid-section, around the stomach energy center; and in the abdomen, around the small intestine energy center, also known as the *hara* chakra. These chakras can also be referred to as "energy furnaces."

Fevers result when the energy within these furnaces becomes excessive. The body receives energy from the environment—in the form of food, light, heat, and various other types of radiation. In normal circumstances, a child discharges unused factors through urination, bowel movement, breathing, and through the skin. Children also constantly discharge through activity and the maintenance of normal body temperature, through which a great deal of heat is continually generated.

When the child's intake becomes excessive, then a variety of abnormal discharge mechanisms may take place. Fever is one of the more common mechanisms for the discharge of excess. In many cases, simple fevers occur when children become constipated. When the abdominal energy center becomes blocked or stagnated, excess begins to accumulate and discharge through other channels, including fever.

The intake of more extreme yang foods such as meat, eggs, salt, poultry, and fish can produce fever. Fever can also result from the intake of more extreme yin items such as sugar, tropical fruits, soda, honey, and other concentrated sweeteners, ice cream, spices, chocolate, and soft drinks. Foods that cause constipation, such as creamy flour cereals, oily, greasy or sticky foods, nut butters, and baked flour products can also produce fever.

General Adjustments in Diet: When a child experiences a fever, first assess his or her overall condition to determine the possible causes and hopefully rule out a specific disorder or emergency such as heatstroke. Also, please note that if the child has not had the measles, it is better to deal with fevers as if they were the first sign of this illness. If the measles are handled improperly, in some cases, more serious complications may result, especially if the fever is mistakenly suppressed. When this is done, rather than allowing the measles to naturally discharge, they go deep inside the body. The risk of a more serious complication is increased when this happens. Please refer to the section on measles for suggestions on handling the measles properly. Additional information is also included in *Macrobiotic Pregnancy and Care of the Newborn*.

Children with fevers can eat according to the standard macrobiotic diet with appropriate adjustments for their age and condition. The dietary extremes that underlie the condition can be reduced or eliminated. If, for example, a child drinks several cups of fruit juice daily or often eats sweetened desserts or oily snacks, these items may need to be avoided until the fever subsides. Even after the fever disappears, it may be necessary to limit the child's intake of these items to prevent discharges from occurring in the future. If you determine that the fever is due to too many salty or baked foods or a lack of fresh foods, the child may need to be put temporarily on a salt-free diet or the amount of salt used in cooking may need to be substantially reduced. You may also want to reduce the child's intake of overly cooked or baked dishes, and include quickly steamed greens, boiled salads and other lightly cooked vegetable dishes on a daily basis.

As we have mentioned, fevers often result from constipation. Foods such as whole grain breads or muffins with peanut or sesame butter can cause stagnation in the digestive tract and lead to constipation. When this occurs, cooked whole grain dishes—including snacks such as sushi or rice balls—are best substituted for bread or flour products, while nuts and nut butters are best avoided until the condition improves. Occasional snacks of *udon* or other whole grain noodles are easiest to digest and may be preferable to flour products, while *arepa* made with whole corn, or sweet rice mochi can also be used as snacks.

Special Dishes and Preparations: In addition to modifying the child's overall diet, the following special dishes and beverages are often helpful in relieving simple fevers. (Please consult the *Recipe and Home Care Guide* in Chapter Five for instructions on preparing these special teas and dishes.)

1. *Special rice cream*—Children can be given one or two small bowls of special rice cream—served hot—in addition to their regular rice and other foods. In cases where the child's condition has become overly yang—i.e., tight and contracted—a small amount of rice syrup or high quality barley malt can be added. If the child's condition is overly yin, a tiny piece (1/4 or 1/3) of an umeboshi plum or a small amount (1/4 teaspoon) of children's gomashio may be added. The use of salt or salty condiments should of course be consistent with our earlier recommendations for adding salt to children's diets.

2. *Dried daikon tea*—When adults or older children experience a fever, a cup or two of tea made with grated raw daikon with a few drops of tamari (see below) can be used to help reduce it. However, this tea is too strong for infants and small children (i.e., under the age of five). Dried daikon tea can be used instead. Children over the age of two can drink up to half a cup of dried daikon tea. Younger children should receive no more than one or two teaspoons of the tea.

3. *Shiitake tea*—Children may also be given the liquid from boiled dried mushrooms, or shiitake, in place of dried daikon tea. The quantity should be similar to that for dried daikon tea.

4. *Dried daikon/shiitake tea*—A third tea, made from the combination of both ingredients, may also be offered in place of the above. The quantities can be the same as above.

5. *Grated daikon tea*—Children over the age of six can receive freshly grated daikon tea. A small cupful should be sufficient.

6. *Grated sour apple*—Raw green apple can help offset fever by releasing stagnated energy, especially in the stomach and intestines. Half of the apple can be used to make fresh juice and half to make applesauce. The juice helps to dissipate stagnation in the stomach; the grated applesauce releases stagna-

tion in the intestines. Babies can receive a teaspoon or so of the juice and children can receive the juice and gratings from an entire apple.

7. *Cereal grain tea*—Brown rice or barley tea can be given to the child in place of, or as one of their normal beverages.

Home Care: Fever is a mechanism through which the body releases excess and maintains harmony with the environment. It is not, as is commonly thought, a "defense" against disease. The body does not "fight" illness in the way that opposing armies clash on the battlefield. Bacteria and viruses are not our enemies but are the natural products of excess. Fever helps the body discharge these and other excessive products. For example, fever stimulates the release of chemicals known as *pyrogens*, which in turn stimulate white blood cells to eliminate virus and bacteria. The white blood cells do not "fight" viruses and bacteria, rather they eat them. Physiologists refer to this function as *phagocytosis*, from the Greek *phagein*, "to eat." The body's immune response is actually an internal eating mechanism; it is no more violent than a plant drawing nutrients from the soil or a human enjoying a meal. If we eat excessively, then the white blood cells are kept busy eating the products of our excess, including viruses and bacteria. The concept of the immune system "fighting" infection is actually a profound misconception. The presence of fever is a positive thing. It shows that a child's power to discharge is strong and functioning properly.

Giving aspirin routinely for simple fevers weakens the body's natural discharging powers. Aspirin is extremely yin and paralyzes the power to expel excess, so discharge symptoms such as coughing or fever stop. The entire body becomes weaker as a result and it takes more time to recover and return to a normal, healthy state.

In general, it is better not to suppress the fever. It makes more sense to allow the excess to be eliminated from the body. The following natural applications can help ease discomfort. At the same time, they do not weaken or interfere with the process of discharge.

1. *External applications:* External applications can be used if the child's fever goes higher than 103°F. Instructions for preparing these applications are presented in the *Recipe and Home Care Guide*. Below are general suggestions on how to use them. It is recommended that parents who are unfamiliar with these applications contact a macrobiotic center or instructor before using them.

1) *Green vegetable plaster*—The green vegetable plaster, made from finely chopped, raw green vegetables, is very mild and can be applied to the forehead for a short while until the temperature begins to drop. Or it can be left on until it becomes warm and then replaced with a fresh application.

2) *Tofu/green vegetable plaster*—A plaster made by combining raw green vegetables and fresh tofu can be applied to the forehead instead of the green vegetable plaster. It can also be left on until the temperature drops or until

it absorbs heat and becomes warm. A fresh plaster can be applied if needed.

3) *Tofu plaster*—A plaster made with fresh tofu is somewhat stronger than the above applications that include greens. For that reason, we recommend not using it on children under the age of two. Milder applications are usually sufficient for younger children. The tofu plaster can be applied in the same manner as above.

As mentioned previously, it is better not to apply plasters if a child has not yet had the measles. After a child has had the measles, however, external applications can be used when a simple fever becomes uncomfortably high.

2. *Adjustments in the environment:* Children with a fever may lose fluid through perspiration. It is better to keep their room slightly moister and warmer than usual and for them to avoid chilling drafts. The air can be moistened by putting a pot or two of steaming water in a corner of the room. Humidifiers or electric steam vaporizers can also be used. Water can be heated on an electric hot plate or moist towels can be put on a radiator.

Figure 8 Applying Tofu Plaster for Fever

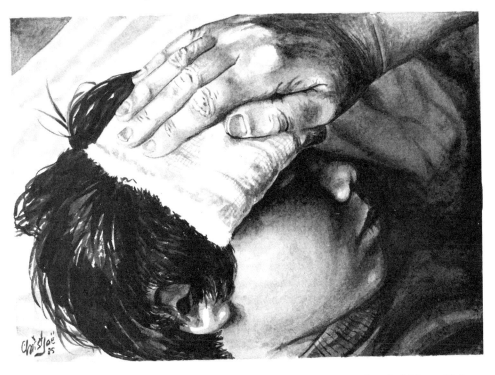

Children can drink rice, barley, or bancha tea to make up for fluid loss. It is important to prevent chilling. Keep the child well-dressed with cotton clothing and covered with blankets. For fevers that are localized in the head and neck, keep the rest of the body covered and warm. If the child develops chills, apply a warm roasted salt pack to the abdomen. (Roast salt in a dry skillet until it becomes hot and wrap it in thick cotton linen or put it in a pillowcase and wrap a cotton towel around it. Allow the pack to cool slightly before applying it to the abdomen.) It is usually better to avoid cold water baths or alcohol rubs as a normal practice. These methods can shock the child's system and can produce chilling. They can also cause the excess to be discharged toward the inside. If the child develops cold hands or feet, rub them gently with a facecloth that has been dipped in warm water.

Palm Healing: Palm healing can help reduce discomfort by allowing excessive energy to discharge more smoothly. In our other family health volume, *Macrobiotic Pregnancy and Care of the Newborn*, we introduce the use of palm healing in a variety of childhood disorders. Also included are exercises to generate healing power. Please refer to this book for further information.

When practicing palm healing, it is important to keep a straight but comfortable posture. It is not necessary to press the palms firmly on the area that you wish to treat. A light, gentle touch is better. Below are several simple methods for easing the discomfort of a fever.

1. *Applying palms to the forehead.*   To help release energy in the forehead, have a child lie on his or her back, covered as usual. Place one hand lightly on the forehead. Close the eyes and breathe quietly and gently, keeping the hand lightly on the forehead. The sound of "Su" may be added on the exhalation. Slowly remove your hand after 15 to 20 minutes.

2. *Applying palms to the front and back of the head.*   As a variation of the above, place one hand on the forehead and the other directly opposite to it on the back of the head. Breathe as above and hold the hands lightly in this position for 15 to 20 minutes.

3. *Applying palms to the intestines.*   As mentioned previously, many fevers are related to blockage in the intestines. To help relieve stagnation or to help excessive energy discharge, have the child lie on his or her back. Sit near the child with a straight but relaxed posture. Breathe normally and quietly and place one hand lightly on the abdomen, so that the center of the palm covers the area just below the navel. Make sure that the child remains properly covered. Breathe as above and apply your palm for 15 to 20 minutes.

4. *Applying palms to the forehead and intestines.*   The lower regions of the body coordinate with the upper regions. An imbalance in one region affects the other. Stagnation in the intestines, for example, often produces elevated temperatures in the forehead or in some cases, headache and tension in the shoulders and neck. (For the same reason, menstrual problems also frequently cause headaches or emotional tension.) The palms can be applied to both regions in order to release stagnation and harmonize the flow of energy

in both regions and the body as a whole. This method is especially helpful for fevers caused by intestinal disorders.

Place one hand on the forehead, as in number one above, and the other hand on the lower abdomen, as in number three. Breathe as described above and continue for 15 to 20 minutes. Be careful to prevent the child from becoming chilled.

Enemas: If a child experiences fever due to constipation, a simple enema often brings relief. In many cases, an enema will cause the fever to drop and make other special applications unnecessary.

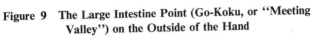

Figure 9 **The Large Intestine Point (Go-Koku, or "Meeting Valley") on the Outside of the Hand**

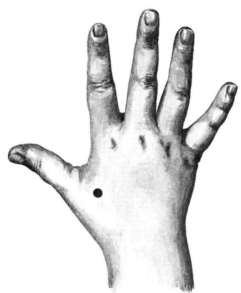

Massage: Gentle stimulation of the large intestine point on the outside of the hand (see Figure 9) can also be helpful in bringing relief from constipation. Press the point gently with the thumb and rub with a circular motion. Massage the points on each hand off and on for about 5 minutes. However, remember that children are much more sensitive than adults. Use only very light pressure. It is recommended that massage normally be used only after children have reached the age of two, and even then, only very gently.

Headaches

Headaches are not common among children who eat well. If they do occur, it is usually because of some dietary excess. In some cases, headaches arise together with other discharge symptoms such as sore throat, fever, or abdominal pain.

Headaches often accompany colds and the flu. Some headaches occur along with emotional stress, while others are the result of an injury to the head.

The dietary causes of headaches vary, and depend upon the region of the head that is most affected. Headaches in the front of the head arise from the excessive intake of extremely yin foods such as sugar, candy, ice cream, chocolate, spices, tropical fruits, soft drinks, iced beverages, and drugs and medications. Pain in the side of the head usually results from the overintake of more yin foods that are less extreme, such as ketchup, potatoes, oily chips, mustard, too many fresh fruits, tomatoes, fruit drinks, and nuts and nut butters. Oily or fried foods especially affect this region. Among sweeteners, sugar, honey, and maple syrup—all more extreme—would tend to affect the front of the head. Rice honey and barley malt—which are yin but somewhat less so—would tend to affect the side of the head when eaten in excess.

Children who eat meat, poultry, eggs, or more salty dishes are more prone to tension headaches in the back of the neck and head. These foods also produce tension in the shoulders. The regular consumption of very extreme foods like smoked salmon, bacon, liver, caviar, or eggs can cause headaches deeper inside the head, together with tension in other parts of the body.

Headaches that occur together with the discharge of mucus from the nose or blocked nasal passages often indicate inflammation of the sinuses, or *sinusitis*. The sinuses in the cheeks develop around age six and those in the forehead around age ten. The sinuses can easily become blocked or inflamed when a child eats an imbalanced diet. Mucus in the sinuses often results from the overintake of fatty or oily foods, including milk, ice cream, and other dairy products, oily desserts, or dishes that have a very greasy quality. Excessive sugar intake—whether in the form of refined sugar, honey, maple syrup, and other concentrated sweeteners or in the form of fruits—can also contribute to this condition, and to sinus inflammation. Too much fluid or too many watery foods can promote nasal blockage by causing the tissues in the sinuses and nasal passages to become swollen.

Some children experience migraines, which are more severe than the types of headaches previously discussed. Migraines result when the arteries on the surface of the brain become more yin or swollen and cause pressure to build up. Migraines are often accompanied by nausea and vomiting, and tend to occur in families.

The dietary cause of migraines is the overconsumption of extremely yin foods and beverages. The repeated overconsumption of extremely expansive items causes the peripheral regions of the brain to swell, including the arteries just below the surface of the skull.

General Adjustments in Diet: As with the other common conditions covered in this chapter, it is important to first check your child's overall condition when a headache develops and hopefully rule out a medical emergency. Parents can also ask the child what he or she has been eating. Children with headaches can follow the standard macrobiotic diet with the appropriate adjustments for their age and condition. Any of the extreme foods that underlie the disorder are best avoided.

Parents usually have a good idea what children are eating when they are younger and can spot imbalances more easily. When children get older, they may eat outside more frequently. Questioning them about what they have been eating is therefore helpful when seeking the underlying causes.

General adjustments in diet for the most common types of headaches are presented below, together with special dishes and preparations for use in each case. Since the recommendations vary slightly according to the location of the pain, it is important to ask the child where his head hurts.

1. *For pain that is localized in the front of the head.* More yin items—including concentrated sweeteners, fruit juice, carbonated beverages, icy cold foods or drinks, and others—contribute to front headaches and are best reduced or avoided during a headache in this area. Oily chips and fried foods are also best avoided if this type of headache is being experienced. Children can eat a standard macrobiotic diet appropriate for their age and condition, with care not to overdo the intake of more yin foods and beverages.

   Children who experience more yin headaches need to be careful about the intake of fruit, concentrated sweeteners—including rice honey and barley malt—raw salads, and too much liquid. The overconsumption of flour products can produce stagnation in the intestines and contribute to this condition, as can the intake of nuts, nut butters, and oily foods. Sinus headaches are often the result of the overintake of milk, ice cream, cheese, sugar, and fruit.

2. *For pain in the sides of the head.* The less extremely yin items mentioned above are best reduced or avoided, together with foods to the far-yin and far-yang. The standard macrobiotic diet—with appropriate adjustments for age and condition—can form the basis of the child's way of eating.

   Oily foods or snacks frequently contribute to this problem. It is better to minimize the use of oil in cooking until the condition improves. Nuts, nut butters, and chips are included in this category, as are oily baked goods. Herbal teas with an aromatic and stimulant effect can also produce pain in the side of the head, and are best avoided.

3. *For tension headaches in the back of the head.* Animal foods or more heavily salted foods or dishes are best reduced or avoided, as are more extremely yin items. The standard macrobiotic diet can be adopted with the necessary modifications for age and condition.

   When children become too tight it is important not to use too much salt, or to serve them heavily salted foods, including snacks and processed items. Overly cooked dishes and baked foods can also contribute to a tight condition.

   In general, the cooking for this condition can be light and fresh. Lightly steamed or boiled vegetables, plus plenty of sweet tasting dishes would be appropriate. A small volume of cooked fruit dessert can be enjoyed from time to time, and concentrated grain sweeteners can be added occasionally.

4. *For pain deep inside the head.* Excessively yang foods are best reduced or

avoided for this condition, and the standard macrobiotic diet with appropriate considerations can be adopted. The suggestions mentioned in number three above can also be considered.

Home Care: When children experience headaches, they may require a period of quiet rest. Headaches are often associated with psychological and emotional stresses that result from dietary imbalances. The intake of more extreme foods weakens the pain control mechanisms in the brain and causes oversensitivity to the normal stresses of daily living. Children who are frequently tired, anxious, or stressed by dietary imbalances are more prone to headaches. Children who frequently experience low level headaches are often depressed as a result of chronic overconsumption of more extremely yin foods and beverages.

When the overall condition becomes unbalanced, factors such as simple pressure changes within the sinuses, changes in blood pressure which produce expansion or contraction in the arteries in the brain, or tension in the neck or shoulders can create a headache.

Along with correcting the child's physical condition through dietary change and home care, parents also need to provide emotional support and reassurance. Parents need to search for any factors in the child's life that may contribute to emotional or psychological unhappiness. If the child is old enough, discussing this matter could be helpful.

The following home applications can also be useful in easing the discomfort of a headache:

1. *For pain in the front or the sides of the head, including migraine headaches.* When headaches arise in this region, dilation of brain cells and blood vessels is the most frequent cause. Cold applications—such as a cold towel—can be applied to the forehead or top and sides of the head. Cold towels can be repeatedly applied for 10 to 15 minutes.
2. *For tension headaches in the back of and deep inside the head.*   Tension headaches caused by tension in the neck and shoulders can often be eased by applying warm towels to the back of the head and neck. Tension headaches deep inside the head—often the result of constriction of the arteries that nourish the brain, and of the brain tissues—can frequently be helped by wrapping a warm towel around the neck. Warm towels can be applied repeatedly for 10 to 15 minutes.
3. *For sinus headaches.*   Sinus blockage can often be relieved by applying a warm towel or washcloth in the manner described above to the forehead— above the eyes and nose—and to each of the cheekbones. Severe, chronic sinus blockage in older children can be loosened by applying a lotus root plaster. Directions for preparing the lotus root plaster are presented in the book, *Macrobiotic Home Remedies.*

Palm Healing: Palm healing is especially helpful in easing headaches. Aside from restoring a more normal balance of energy, it establishes a soothing emotional bond between parent and child. It helps to relieve stress, tension, and anxiety and helps children relax and calm down.

The following methods can be used in easing headaches:

1. *For pain in the front of the head.* This application can be done with the child sitting in a comfortable, relaxed position. Sit facing the child's side. Keep a straight but relaxed posture. Extend the arms and place one palm on the forehead and one palm directly opposite on the back of the head. Close the eyes and breathe with a quiet, gentle rhythm. The sound of "Su" may also be added on the exhalation. Remove the hands after 15 to 20 minutes.

2. *For headaches caused by blocked sinuses.* This application is divided into two procedures. In the first, the palms are applied to loosen stagnation in the general area of the sinuses. In the second, energy is focused on specific points within the sinuses.

   Begin by placing one hand gently over the eyes so that the center of the palm covers the bridge of the nose. Place the other hand directly opposite on the back of the head. Breathe as above and apply the palms for 5 to 7 minutes. (This method can also be used to relieve discomfort due to eye-strain.)

Figure 10   Points for Relief of Sinus Blockage

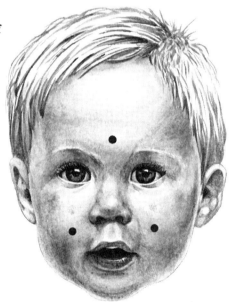

Then lightly apply the fingers of one hand to the sinus points illustrated in Figure 10. (Use the thumb, the index, and the middle or ring fingers.) Place the other hand on the back of the head, opposite to the cheeks and forehead. Close the eyes and breathe with a gentle, quiet rhythm. The sound of "Su" may be added on the exhalation while gently vibrating the fingers. After 10 to 15 minutes, rapidly detach your palm and fingers.

3. *For pain in the side of the head.* Sit or stand (if the child is sitting in a chair) behind the child. Extend the arms and place the palms lightly on the sides of the head or on both sides of the top of the head, if this region is painful. Breathe as above, and apply the palms for 10 to 15 minutes before slowly removing them.

4. *For pain in the back of the head.* Sit next to the child, facing his or her side. Place one hand gently on the region of the back of the head where the pain is centered, the other on the forehead. Breathe as above and remove the hands after 10 to 15 minutes.

5. *For pain deep inside the head.* Pain in the inner regions of the head can be approached in several ways.
   A. Sit behind the child and gently place one hand on top of the head. Breathe as above and remove the hand after 10 to 15 minutes.
   B. Sit behind the child and gently cover both ears with the palms, so that the center of each palm covers the center of each ear. Breathe and continue as above.
   C. Sit facing the child's side and place one hand gently on the back of the head and the other on the forehead. Breathe and continue as above. (This method is similar to number four above.)

If a child becomes distracted before the application is finished, pause a few minutes and then continue. However, it is better for the application to be continuous and without interruption. Therefore, before beginning, help children relax by telling them a short story or by singing them a song. Also, when they are old enough, explain in simple language how palm healing works and how it helps them to feel better. In cases where children are too active to sit still, palm healing can be applied while they are sleeping. Posture can be adjusted when necessary.

Massage and Compresses: Simple, light massage is often helpful in relieving the discomfort of headaches, especially when it is given in combination with warm or cool compresses. One of the most effective ways to restore balance in the flow of energy in the head is to massage points or regions on the energy meridians that run along the face, head, and front of the body. The stomach meridian runs down the front of the body from the face to the second and third toes. It can be massaged when children experience frontal headaches, including sinus and migraine headaches. The gallbladder meridian runs along the side of the head down to the fourth toe. It can be massaged to relieve side headaches. The bladder meridian runs along the back of the head down either side of the spine and along the back of the legs to the fifth toe. It can be used to release tension in the back of the head or neck. Tension or pressure in the center of the head can be relieved through massage on the liver or spleen meridians that run up along the inside of the legs and the front of the body from the first toe.

Stimulating the peripheral areas of the meridians is especially effective in releasing excessive energy in the head. The most peripheral regions of the meridians mentioned above are located on the toes. As we have seen, the fifth toe is an extension of the bladder meridian; the fourth, an extension of the gallbladder; the third and second, extensions of the stomach; and the large toe an extension of the liver and spleen meridians. (Please refer to *The Book of Dō-In: Exercise for Physical and Spiritual Development* by the author for a complete explanation of the meridians and organs.)

1. *For pain in the front of the head, including migraine and sinus headaches.* The child can lie comfortably on the back and relax. Repeatedly apply cold cotton washcloths to the forehead for 5 to 7 minutes. Then gently massage the second toe for several minutes. Do the third toe in a similar manner, and then do both toes at the same time. Massage the toes by gently pulling them outward. After finishing one foot, repeat the same procedure on the other one.

2. *For pain in the side of the head.* Apply cold towels—as above—to the painful area. Then massage the fourth toe of each foot as instructed above.

3. *For tension headaches in the back of the head.* Your child can lie comfortably on the front with head turned to the side. Apply repeated warm towels or a cotton washcloth to the painful region as above. Then massage the fifth toe of each foot as indicated above.

4. *For tension headaches deep inside the head.* The child can lie comfortably on the back. Apply a hot squeezed towel or washcloth around the neck. Replace with a fresh application as the first one cools and continue for 5 minutes. Then massage the large toe on each foot as described above.

These applications are safe and effective and do not expose children to artificial substances. The majority of simple childhood headaches can be relieved through simple applications such as these, along with attention to proper diet.

Stomachache

When children eat a naturally balanced diet, stomachaches seldom occur. If they do arise, it is usually because the child ate some type of extreme or unbalanced food, or perhaps ate too rapidly or too much.

Stomachaches can be caused by the intake of too many constrictive items—such as eggs, poultry, fish, salt, meat, and baked foods —or by a lack of freshness or variety in the diet. More extremely yang foods can cause the stomach energy center, or chakra, to become tight and contracted. The stomach, liver, gallbladder, spleen, and pancreas often become tighter and their function may stagnate. The intake of these more extremely yang foods tends to affect the contracted lower portion of the stomach and the duodenum more than the expanded body of the stomach.

The intake of more extremely yin items can also cause stomach pains or cramps. The overintake of cold or iced foods or beverages, raw fruit, oily snacks or chips, including fried foods, concentrated sweeteners, spices, and vegetables such as tomatoes and potatoes may produce this reaction. In this case, energy in the stomach chakra becomes weak and diffused. Overeating or lack of proper chewing can also produce this condition. The intake of excessively yin foods tends to affect the expanded body of the stomach rather than the more contracted regions.

Two foods which are common in children's diets today can be especially troublesome. The consumption of cow's milk and its products frequently causes stomach and digestive upset. *Lactose intolerance*, or the inability to digest milk products, is a common cause of stomach and intestinal discomfort. Common symptoms include stomachache, bloating, and diarrhea. Repeated overconsumption produces an overall weakening of the stomach and intestines.

Refined sugar—including concentrated sweeteners such as honey and maple syrup—also produces stomach problems. When sugar enters the stomach, it temporarily paralyzes the organ. As little as a quarter teaspoon of sugar can cause this reaction. Refined sugar is an extremely alkaloid substance and causes the stomach to secrete a large amount of acid in order to maintain a normal balance. An over-acidic stomach is a frequent cause of discomfort.

The intake of extremes of either yin or yang can sometimes produce an inflammation in the digestive organs, a condition known as *gastroenteritis*. This condition can result in cramp-like pains in the stomach or intestines, sometimes along with vomiting and diarrhea.

Abdominal pain can occur by itself or together with other symptoms. Children with sore throats or colds may also complain of stomachaches. Emotional factors, including stress or anxiety, also play a role. However, dietary imbalances usually underlie many stress-related conditions, including stomachache. (Please refer to *Macrobiotic Pregnancy and Care of the Newborn* for a discussion of diarrhea, constipation, colic and other digestive disorders.)

General Adjustments in Diet: When children experience stomachaches, it is helpful to review their overall condition. In this way, the underlying cause can more easily be determined. Hopefully, a specific emergency requiring medical attention such as appendicitis, poisoning, or the presence of a foreign object in the stomach can be ruled out.

For children who normally eat macrobiotically, stomachaches can arise as the result of (1) recurring excesses in their diets, as for example in cases where a child regularly binges on sugared snacks, perhaps at school or with friends; or from (2) the occasional or one-time intake of some extreme or unbalanced food, for example, as in the case where a child eats too much cake or snacks at a birthday party.

Parents may need to ask the child questions so as to find out what the cause of the problem is. In most cases, the condition will improve once the problem food or foods are identified and removed from the diet. Recovery is usually fairly rapid once the child begins to eat the appropriate standard macrobiotic diet, perhaps with the addition of a few special dishes or teas.

Another type of disorder comes about when children eat an extremely unbalanced diet as a normal practice. In these cases, changing the cause of the condition involves reorienting the diet as a whole. Recurring stomachaches, headaches, colds, or other chronic health problems are the result of repeated dietary imblances. In these cases, it is recommended that parents consider changing their way of eating toward the standard macrobiotic diet, with appropriate adjustments for each member of the family.

For stomach disorders in general, millet can be frequently served. Of course, brown rice and other whole grains can be eaten as well. Millet can be pressure-cooked together with rice, prepared with vegetables such as squash or carrots, served in soups, or as a soft breakfast cereal. Round, sweet-tasting vegetables such as fall or winter squashes, onions, and cabbage can also be helpful and soothing for stomach discomfort. These vegetables can be served nishime style, or in soups or stews. Millet-squash soup is often useful in soothing stomach discomfort.

A small volume of such items as umeboshi plum, sauerkraut, or sour pickles—like those made with umeboshi vinegar—can help quiet an overactive stomach. A small portion can be given to the child in the form of condiments. However, remember that they contain salt, so use them in very small quantities and only for children who have already begun to eat a small amount of salt in their diets.

Special Dishes and Preparations: Among special macrobiotic drinks, several can be useful in relieving discomfort in the stomach and digestive organs, including the small and large intestines. These preparations are especially helpful in neutralizing an overly acidic condition. They should be given only to children who have already begun to use a small volume of salt in their diets.

1. *Ume-sho-kuzu (kudzu) drink*—Children can take a small cup of *ume-sho-kuzu* drink for one to three days. For smaller children, use only a tiny piece of umeboshi plum and a few drops of tamari. The drink should be much milder than that normally used by adults. Older children can use up to half of a plum.
2. *Ume-sho-bancha*—A small teacup of *ume-sho-bancha* can be given in place of ume-sho-kuzu. Again, use only a tiny piece of umeboshi plum and one or two drops of tamari soy sauce for smaller children.
3. *Ume-bancha tea*—Umeboshi plums can be used by themselves in bancha tea to help relieve stomach or intestinal discomfort. Again, use only a tiny piece of plum for small children.
4. *Baked umeboshi plums or pits*—Older children—above the age of six—can receive bancha tea in which 1/4 to 1/3 teaspoon of baked, powdered umeboshi plum or pits are dissolved. This special tea can be given once in two days only.

Other special dishes, including soft cooked cereals—such as soft rice or millet—can be substituted for regular grains for several days until the condition improves. The *special rice cream* introduced in the section on fever can also be used.

In some cases, the specific dietary cause of stomach or intestinal discomfort can be pinpointed. If you are able to trace the condition to the toxic effects of a specific food or category of foods, you can then prepare macrobiotic dishes to help offset these effects. These special dishes can be added to the daily diet, with the appropriate considerations for age and condition. Again, the use of salt should be consistent with our earlier suggestions. Dishes that contain salt should not be given to children who have not yet begun to include salt in their diets.

1. *For stomachaches caused by dairy products:*
   - *Light mugi miso soup with wakame and scallions.* This particular soup can be served along with meals for several days. Children may drink 1/2 to 1 cup per day.
   - *Onions cooked with squash or Hokkaido pumpkin.* This dish can be served as part of a meal for several days.
   - *Nori condiment.* When preparing nori condiment for children, use a very small amount of tamari soy sauce, much less than for adults (see recipe section). Children can eat 1/2 teaspoon of nori condiment for several consecutive days or several times over the course of a week. A small amount of grated fresh ginger can be added when the digestive upset is the result of eating cheese.
   - *Daikon, daikon leaves and kombu.* This dish can be prepared nishime style and served along with meals several times per week.

2. *For stomachaches caused by meat, poultry, or fish:*
   - *Pearl barley soup.*
   - *Light miso soup with onions and scallions.*
   These soups can be served daily for several days in addition to other soups that are included in the child's diet.
   - *Shiitake mushroom.* Shiitake can be added to soups and vegetable dishes or can be used in making shiitake mushroom tea. Children can receive several cups of tea over the course of several days.
   - *Grated daikon.* An older child (over six) with stomach or intestinal pain caused by eating meat or poultry can receive a small amount (several teaspoons) of grated raw daikon with one or two drops of tamari added. It can be given once a day for three days. Younger children can receive the milder dried daikon teas mentioned in the discussion of fever.
   - *Green leafy vegetables.* Kale, watercress, daikon or turnip greens can be quickly steamed or boiled and served everyday as a part of the child's diet.
   For stomach or digestive pains caused by eating too many eggs, a small amount of either sauerkraut, umeboshi vinegar, cooked daikon, or daikon pickles will often help bring relief. Again, please remember the appropriate considerations about giving children salt or salty foods. A small volume of light miso soup with scallions can also be included in the diet for several days. Digestive upsets caused by eating shellfish can be offset by adding a small amount of grated ginger to vegetable dishes or to soups, or, for older children, by giving them several tablespoons of grated raw daikon or raw radish with one or two drops of tamari. A small amount of brown rice or other grain vinegar can be used for several days in salad dressing or as a condiment to help offset the effects of shellfish. Stomachaches caused by

eating fish can be offset by serving several dishes of cooked daikon or mustard greens, or by seasoning one or two dishes with a small amount of grated ginger or umeboshi or grain vinegar. *Shiso* (beefsteak) leaves are also helpful in relieving stomachaches caused by eating too much fish.

3. *For stomachaches caused by sugar:* Any of the following special drinks may be used by children who are old enough to be using salt in their diets:
   - *Mild tamari/bancha tea.*
   - *Mild ume-sho-bancha tea.*
   - *Any of the umeboshi teas mentioned above.*

   As discussed earlier, these beverages should be very mild, and should not be given to children who are not using a small amount of salt already. Use only several drops of tamari or a small piece of umeboshi plum when preparing them. Use only one of these teas once a day for several days.

   The following dishes can be added to the child's diet, again, with the appropriate consideration of their age and condition:
   - *Sea vegetable dishes.* Hijiki is especially recommended. Children can receive a small, mildly seasoned side dish for several days. Arame, wakame, kombu and nori can also be used in a variety of dishes. The minerals in sea vegetables help to offset the effects of sugar. Children's sea vegetables should be very mildly seasoned.
   - *Azuki-kombu-squash.* Children can receive a small serving of this dish once a day for several days. It should be more mildly seasoned than that eaten by adults.

Home Care: Since stomachaches frequently occur with emotional problems or upsets, it is important to provide children with a loving, supportive, and warm home environment. If a specific problem or situation is bothering them, please discuss it and help them to find a solution. Love and reassurance can be powerful forces in keeping children healthy.

The child can be scrubbed daily with a warm towel or warm ginger towel. Scrub gently until the skin becomes slightly red.

Repeated warm towels may be applied to the abdomen for 10 to 15 minutes or a hot water bottle or a warm roasted salt pack may be applied instead. Make sure that they are not too hot.

Palm Healing: When the stomach or intestinal energy centers become overly tight or contracted, applying the palms can help loosen and energize them. The right palm, which conducts more of earth's expanding force, is generally more effective for this purpose. When the digestive energy centers become overly expanded or weak, applying the palms can help strengthen and consolidate them. The left palm conducts more of heaven's descending energy and is generally more effective for this purpose.

Any of the following methods can be applied when children experience discomfort in the stomach or intestines:

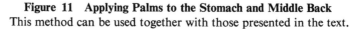

Figure 11   Applying Palms to the Stomach and Middle Back
This method can be used together with those presented in the text.

1. *Applying palms to the stomach energy center (stomach chakra).*   The child
    can lie comfortably on the back. The parents should have a straight but
    relaxed posture. Breathe normally and quietly and place one hand lightly on
    the solar plexus just below the breastbone or sternum. The center of the
    palm should be placed directly over this spot. Breathe as described previously
    and keep the palm in place for 15 to 20 minutes. Make sure that the child is
    properly covered during the application.

2. *Applying the palms to the stomach energy center and the second and third
    toes.*   This application is based on the complementary/antagonistic relation-
    ship that exists between the inner regions of the body and the periphery.

    The child can lie comfortably on the back, as above. Place one hand on
    the abdomen—as above—and with the thumb and fingers of the other hand,
    lightly grasp the second and third toes. (Either foot is fine.) The parent can
    close his or her eyes and breathe quietly and gently. The sound of "Su"
    may be added if desired. After about 5 to 7 minutes, release the second and
    third toes and gently grasp those of the other foot. Keep the other hand in
    the same position on the abdomen. Continue for another 5 to 7 minutes and
    then remove both hands.

3. *Applying palms to the intestines and forehead.*   The methods presented in

the discussion of fever (number three and four) for treating the intestines can also be used for discomfort in the lower digestive tract.

Massage: Gently stimulating the stomach meridian can help ease discomfort in that organ. When energy is excessive, massage can help to discharge it more smoothly. When energy is deficient, it can help in supplying energy.

Have the child lie comfortably with feet on the floor and knees raised. The stomach meridian runs down the outside-front of both legs to the second and third toes.

Sit facing the child's legs. Gently grip the leg with the thumb on the inside and the fingers opposite to it on the outside. Beginning just below the knee, use the fingers to press down the stomach meridian on the leg and then across the top of the foot to the second and third toes. Use the thumb to support the fingers. The legs and feet can be massaged simultaneously or one at a time.

When massaging the stomach meridian, stop in the area of the *San-Ri* point (stomach 36) located on the outside of the leg below the knee. With the index and middle fingers, give extra massage to this point. Use a rotating, circular motion and massage the point for several minutes before proceeding down the meridian.

The second and third toes can be massaged once the meridians have been treated. To do this, straighten the child's leg and hold the foot by placing one hand under the heel. Use the thumb and index finger of the other hand to gently grasp

Figure 12   San-Ri (Stomach 36)

each toe. Begin at the base of the toe and with a gentle, pinching motion, work outward to the tip. Then pull and rotate the toe and pull and snap the fingers gently off the tip. Repeat this procedure on the two toes of each foot that are part of the stomach meridian.

Colds and Flu

The average child today has as many as eight colds a year, an indication that our modern diet and lifestyle have become increasingly unnatural. Children between the ages of three to six usually have more colds than older or younger children.

Colds are much less frequent among children who eat a naturally balanced diet. Colds represent the discharge of excess in the diet. The accumulation and discharge of excess often provides fertile ground for one of the over one hundred cold viruses that have been identified so far.

The symptoms of a cold are usually nasal discharge—including a runny nose—sneezing, coughing, and fever that usually does not exceed 102°F. Some children develop pink, watery eyes and a slight whitish-yellow eye discharge. Irregular bowel movements and sometimes diarrhea may accompany colds.

Influenza, or the "flu," includes many of these symptoms, along with body aches, vomiting, diarrhea, flushing of the neck, face, and chest, and headache.

Colds primarily involve the upper respiratory organs—the throat, sinuses, and nasal passages. The flu also affects these areas, but usually produces more generalized symptoms throughout the body. In some cases, it involves the digestive organs, a condition commonly known as "intestinal flu."

When the discharge of a cold involves the upper body—for example, the nasal passages, head, and throat—the primary cause is the overintake of excessive yin items. These can include simple sugars, concentrated sweeteners, fruit and fruit juice, spices, tomatoes, potatoes, and other highly acidic vegetables, soft drinks, ice cream, and too much liquid. When the discharge affects the lungs and middle section of the body, including the stomach, the primary cause is the overintake of the more yin items mentioned above plus fats and oils, including those in dairy products, poultry, and other animal foods. Discharges that affect the small and large intestines are caused by the overintake of more heavy animal fats in addition to the items mentioned above.

Colds tend to be more prevalent during the autumn and winter, and there are good reasons why this is so. The diets of many people today do not reflect natural seasonal variations which could help them adjust to changing weather conditions. In addition, during the colder months, the air in many homes becomes unnaturally warm and dry. This creates a considerable difference between indoors and outdoors. The unusually hot and dry condition inside the home causes many children (and adults) to consume a large amount of more extremely yin items, including ice cream, cold soft drinks, tropical fruits, sugar, and fruit juices. These foods cause their condition to become disharmonious with the outside environment. One result is to lower resistance to the colder outside temperatures and to the numerous viruses and bacteria that exist naturally in the environment.

Some children experience continual colds and flu during the winter, while others are rarely affected. Yet both groups are frequently exposed to the same general pool of viruses in the environment. Why is it that some children are greatly affected while others only slightly or not at all? The differences in resistance must be due to a deeper underlying factor, for example, daily dietary practice. The daily diet either strengthens or weakens natural resistance, and raises or lowers the threshold of infection. The key to preventing colds is found more in avoiding the extremes in diet that lead to recurring discharges and lowered resistance than it is in isolating ourselves from the many viruses and bacteria that are naturally present in the environment. Strengthening the natural powers of resistance through an environmentally balanced diet is the most direct way to prevent these common conditions.

Colds and flu typically follow a natural course. They represent a movement of excessive energy within the body. The typical cold cycle begins with a more yin, expansive, and outward phase, and finishes with a more yang, inward or consolidated phase. The more yin phase is commonly called the *acute* or *early stage* of a cold. It generally lasts for three or four days, during which time excess begins to accumulate and is discharged through the upper respiratory tract. The discharge is at first usually watery and loose, and the cold virus takes root in and spreads throughout the mucous membranes of the nose and throat. Fever begins during this stage and the child may start to discharge through coughing.

Once the initial stage has been completed, the cold cycle enters a phase of consolidation and resolution. This is commonly known as the *late stage* of a cold. The thin, watery discharge usually becomes thicker and yellowish in color. The immune system begins to resist further spread of the virus, and appetite and energy start to return. Swollen, inflamed mucous membranes gradually return to a more contracted, normal state. Coughing usually continues through this stage, and may be worse in the evening during the time when energy in the lungs and large intestine is normally more active.

Ultimately, more normal discharge processes take over the elimination of remaining excess. Discharge is then accomplished through the kidneys, skin, lungs, and intestines. At this time the cold resolves itself and the child returns to a normal condition.

The flu normally follows a similar cycle lasting from three days to a week. In some cases, however, one cycle is not enough to discharge accumulated excess, and several flu cycles may occur one after the other. Symptoms sometimes disappear after several days and then return unexpectedly.

These cycles can be subdivided into the five general stages as shown in Figure 13. The stages of *onset* and *acute symptoms* represent more yin, or expansive phases, while *gathering*, *consolidation*, and *resolution* are more yang phases.

Colds tend to occur with greater frequency among children than adults. Children are generally more sensitive to the effects of food and environment. Their condi-

Figure 13   The Cycle of the Common Cold

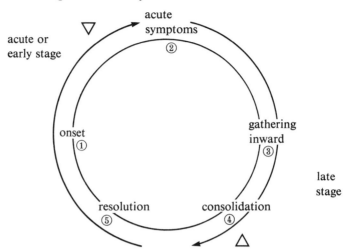

tions change rapidly from day to day and moment to moment. Excess tends to discharge more quickly. Adults usually have many more years of excessive diet behind them. Their ability to discharge is often less efficient. Rather than discharging, excess tends to accumulate in the internal organs and throughout the body, leading eventually to a degenerative disorder of some kind.

When children have a chronically unbalanced blood condition, the bacteria normally found in the mucous membranes may rapidly develop during a cold. A *secondary infection* may then develop, with possible additional complications such as ear infection, sinusitis, sore throat, laryngitis, and, in rare instances, pneumonia.

These complications originate with a chronically unbalanced condition in the blood and body fluids that results from an extreme diet. Children who eat macrobiotically generally have fewer colds. Because their overall condition is generally healthy and well-balanced, when colds occur, they are usually minor and without complication. They normally improve with the help of just slight changes in diet and simple home care.

General Adjustments in Diet: Children often want to eat less when they have a cold, especially during the first several days. Instead of trying to force them to eat, it is better to have a variety of simply prepared dishes available for when they feel hungry. Children with colds can generally follow the standard guidelines that are appropriate for their age and condition.

Grains may be more appealing when they are soft-cooked or are served in soups. Soft-cooked rice *(rice kayu)* or millet are often preferred, as are rice, millet or barley soups with vegetables. It is generally advisable to limit or avoid the intake of flour products—including bread, muffins, cookies, and creamy, floury cereals. However, whole grain noodles or a slice or two of unyeasted sourdough bread may be served occasionally. Light miso soup and tamari broth soups may also be eaten if desired.

It is better to avoid the intake of raw salad and also oil during the recovery period. Vegetables can be lightly steamed, boiled, cooked nishime style, water sautéed, or served in soups and stews. Sweet tasting vegetables, including squash, cabbage, onions, daikon, and carrots are especially recommended, although other varieties can also be included.

Bean and sea vegetable dishes may be served as usual. Fish is best avoided during recovery, although a small amount of low fat white-meat fish may be eaten if desired. Raw fruits and fruit juices are best avoided. Sweet tasting desserts can be made with cooked apples and other seasonal fruits. Rice or amazaké pudding may also be served. It is better to avoid the use of concentrated sweeteners during a cold.

Children may enjoy the usual macrobiotic snacks, although nuts and nut butters are best temporarily avoided. It is also better to avoid juices, sparkling waters and other more yin beverages during a cold. Bancha twig and cereal grain teas are preferable. Cold or iced foods or beverages are also best avoided. Everything should be hot, warm, or room temperature. An occasional small cup of hot apple juice may be included.

As the cold begins to run its course, the child can begin to resume his or her normal way of eating. However, it is better to stay within the above guidelines until all symptoms disappear and the child returns to a completely normal condition.

Special Dishes and Preparations: It is important to remember that the measles begin with symptoms that resemble colds and flu (red, watery eyes, loss of appetite, fatigue, fever and a hard, dry cough). Therefore, if the child has not had the measles, we recommend waiting to see whether a rash develops before giving special dishes or doing external applications, especially those which aid in fever control. If it turns out that the child is developing a case of measles, the situation is best dealt with differently. It is generally better not to give special drinks or external applications for measles. (Please refer to our discussion later in this chapter or in *Macrobiotic Pregnancy and Care of the Newborn* for advice about how to proceed.)

If the child has had the measles, the following special dishes and beverages can be used in easing the discomfort of colds or flu.

1. *To help ease coughing and nasal discharge.*
   - *Lotus root tea.*   Tea made from grated fresh lotus root can be helpful in easing respiratory congestion. Small children can receive 1/3 to 1/2 cup; older children can drink a full cup. Lotus root tea can be given once a day for several days or during the time that a child is coughing.
2. *To help ease digestive discomfort, tiredness, and aches and pains.*
   - *Ume-sho-kuzu drink.*   The powdered kuzu root drink described in the discussion of stomachache can be used to restore vitality and ease digestive upset, including diarrhea. The drink can be given for one to three days. Small children can have 1/4 to 1/3 cup, older children 1/2 to 1 cup.

(Children who have not yet started to use salt should not be given this preparation.) The drink should be milder than for adults. Ume-sho-kuzu can also help restore appetite.

3. *To help reduce fever.* The special teas described in the section on fever can be given. To repeat, if a child has not had measles, please wait until it can be determined that the cold is not actually the onset of measles before preparing the special drinks and dishes.

Home Care: Children can rest at home during the first three to four days of a cold. It may not be necessary for the child to stay in bed during this time, although if they want to do so, let them. If the weather is mild, a child with a cold can go outside for brief periods if he or she feels strong enough and is properly dressed. However, it is better to wait until the fever disappears before going outside.

If the child's cough makes him uncomfortable, the air in the room can be kept slightly moist by placing a pot or two of steaming water in a corner. Electric steam vaporizers or humidifiers can also be used. An electric hot plate can also be used to heat a pot of water.

The following external applications can also be used to help relieve the discomfort of colds or flu.

1. *For fevers.* The external applications listed in the discussion of fever—including the *green vegetable, tofu/green vegetable,* and *tofu plaster*—can be applied when fevers exceed 103°F. The *roasted salt pack,* also described in that section, can also be applied if a child becomes chilled. Again, do not use these applications if the child has not had the measles.

2. *For headaches.* The compresses and massage described in the discussion of headaches can be applied when necessary, including the recommendations for the relief of blocked sinuses. However, it is better not to apply warm towels to the head or neck while the child is experiencing fever.

3. *For chills, fatigue, or body aches.* Rubbing the child's body with a warm towel or warm ginger towel can help in relieving these conditions. Hot towels are best not applied to the whole body during an active fever.

4. *For diarrhea.* The warm *roasted salt pack* can be applied to the abdomen to help relieve looseness in the bowels. (Make sure the pack is not uncomfortably hot and do not apply it to infants.)

5. *For coughing or congestion in the chest or sinuses.* Warm towels can be applied repeatedly to the chest in order to loosen stagnated mucus. Apply warm towels repeatedly for 10 to 15 minutes. They can also be applied to the sinuses to help relieve stagnation in the nasal passageways.

Palm Healing: Palm healing can be helpful in relieving the discharge symptoms of a cold. The basic techniques have been presented in earlier sections. These include: applications for fever, headache, and stomach or intestinal discomfort. The intestinal applications described in the section on fever can also be used for diarrhea.

For coughing and lung congestion, place one hand across the chest region. Breathe naturally and quietly and keep the hand in place for 10 to 15 minutes. The plams can be applied to each lung separately, or place one hand on the upper back or chest and cover both lungs at the same time.

As a variation, one palm can be placed on the chest and the other on the abdomen in the region of the transverse colon. Breathe and apply as above. In this way, problems in the lungs and large intestine can be dealt with simultaneously.

Earaches

Excess frequently gathers in the middle or inner ear. These excessive factors come primarily from the overconsumption of fruit, fruit juice, sugar and concentrated sweeteners, oily foods, spices, and other more extremely yin items. Animal fats, including those in dairy foods, meat, poultry and eggs can also cause excess to accumulate in the ears.

The ears are especially sensitive to the effects of cold or iced foods or beverages, as are the kidneys. The overconsumption of ice cream, soft drinks, Popsicles, and similar frozen items is a frequent contributor to problems in the ears and kidneys. The overintake of salt or extremely salty foods can also contribute to ear and kidney problems.

Children who consume the modern diet frequently have earaches. One or two earaches a year is not unusual for children today. On the other hand, children who eat a more naturally balanced diet rarely experience earaches. When they do, the underlying dietary causes can usually be readily identified and corrected.

In some cases, the accumulation of excess in the ear leads to the growth of virus or bacteria and to infection. Ear infections are more common when the natural immunity is weakened through the overconsumption of sugar, tropical fruits, drugs and medications, and fatty animal foods. When younger children develop ear infections, they often have fever. Fever is less common among older children with earaches.

The most common site for ear infection is the region behind the eardrum. Infection here is called *otitis media*, or *middle ear infection*. Pain frequently results when accumulated excess, including fluid, mucus, or infection, hampers the normal drainage of the ear through the *eustachian tubes*.

Some children experience feelings of pressure and blockage in the ears for several weeks after an earache has disappeared. They may even experience some temporary loss of hearing. This is often the result of the buildup of liquid and mucus in the middle ear. The eustachian tubes often become blocked as a result.

In some cases, earaches are caused when children put some type of small object into their ears, including beans, stones, paper, and so on. If the object can be seen and grasped easily, it can be carefully and gently removed. If it cannot be easily grasped, or if trying to reach it could result in it being pushed further in, medical assistance is needed. It is also advisable to seek assistance if a child punctures the eardrum with a pencil or other sharp object.

Some children experience a chronic buildup of wax in the ears. Wax is often caused by excessive fats, oils, and sugars in the diet. Milk and other dairy foods, candy, sugared soft drinks, tropical fruits, and oily or greasy foods are often the underlying cause.

Tympanotomy, or the surgical puncturing of the eardrum to allow drainage of fluid, is widespread today. Tympanotomy is now the most common surgery among children, and has surpassed the removal of the tonsils. This procedure is often done in cases of recurrent middle ear infection. However, it does not address the underlying cause of the condition, and can cause such side effects as scarring of the eardrum, hearing loss, and acute middle ear infection. It is recommended that such a drastic procedure be used only in emergencies and after dietary change and home care have first been tried.

General Adjustments in Diet: As with the other conditions presented in this book, simple adjustments in diet can often help in bringing relief. Children who experience an earache can adopt the standard macrobiotic diet –with a wide selection of foods and cooking methods—appropriate to their age and condition. Avoiding or minimizing the foods that contribute to the swelling of the mucous membranes of the middle ear—such as dairy products, sugar, and tropical fruits—helps eliminate the underlying cause. Specific adjustments, such as those recommended for colds and fever may also be helpful when necessary.

Home Care: The following natural applications are often helpful in comforting the pain of an earache:

1. *Chlorophyll plaster*—A cool plaster made with green vegetables can be applied to the painful ear. Hold the plaster gently over the ear and replace it with a fresh plaster when the application becomes warm.
2. *Tofu/green vegetable plaster*—A plaster made by mixing mashed leafy greens, raw tofu, and a small amount of whole wheat pastry flour can be applied in place of the chlorophyll plaster mentioned above. The plaster can be applied to the region of the head directly behind the ear. Hold the plaster gently in place and replace it with a fresh application when the first one becomes warm.
3. *Warm sesame oil drops*– Several drops of warm, specially filtered sesame oil can be put in the ear with an eye-dropper. It is recommended that the cool applications presented above be used together with warm sesame oil drops. However, it is better not to use the sesame oil drops if ear drainage is occurring.
4. *Absorbant cotton* can be put in the ear if the ear is discharging thin, clear liquid. Ear discharges or leakages usually occur when the eardrum tears from the pressure of infection. The tear is usually tiny and will normally heal quickly. It does not necessarily indicate a more serious infection.
5. *Warm towels*—Middle ear problems often occur together with stagnation in the kidneys. Mucus, fat, or liquid may accumulate in the kidneys at the same

time that middle ear pain is being experienced. Repeatedly applying warm towels to the middle back can help loosen and dissolve stagnation in the kidneys. Towels can be warmed under a hot faucet or in a pan of hot water. Adjust the temperature of the towels by waving them back and forth after wringing them out. Younger children should receive a milder, not-so-hot application, while older children can tolerate hotter towels. However, do not make the towel so hot that the child squirms or cries each time it touches the skin. The purpose of the application is to help swollen tissues relax and become more activated. If the child becomes tense or fearful the effectiveness of the application will be diminished.

Palm Healing: Palm healing can be very helpful in comforting an earache or in helping to loosen stagnated mucus in the middle ear. The following simple methods can be used by parents, grandparents, or other members of the family:

1. *Applying the palms to the affected ear:* To comfort the affected ear, place one hand gently over it so that the center of the palm covers the opening of the ear. Breathe as described in the previous sections and detach the hand after 15 to 20 minutes.
2. *Applying palms to both ears:* This method may be used instead of the above. Simply place the palms over both ears so that the center of the palm covers the ear opening. Breathe and continue as above.
3. *Applying palms to the kidneys:* Relieving stagnation or tightness in the kidneys can often be helpful in easing discomfort in the inner ear. To comfort the kidneys, place one hand gently across the kidney region on the back. Breathe and apply as above.
4. *Applying palms to the ears and kidneys*: The ears can be comforted at the same time that we relieve stagnation in the kidneys. Place one hand gently over the ear as described above. Place the other hand on the same side kidney region on the back. (When comforting the right ear, apply the hand to the right kidney; when comforting the left ear, apply to the left kidney.) Breathe and continue as above.

Sore Throats and Tosillitis

The throat is a frequent site for the accumulation of excess which tends to gather here in order to be discharged. These accumulations may or may not be accompanied by the growth of virus or bacteria. The underlying cause of these discharges is the intake of extremes. More extreme yin foods and beverages—sugar, ice cream, cookies, soft drinks, and orange juice—can often lead to accumulation in the throat. The intake of eggs, meat, poultry, and dairy products can also result in throat inflammation.

Children who eat a naturally balanced diet rarely experience sore throats or inflammation of the tonsils or adenoids.

In some cases, sore throats occur together with other symptoms of colds or flu. In many cases, especially when the daily diet is more extreme, excessive factors accumulating in the tissues and glands in the throat create a medium for the growth of viruses. The symptoms of a *viral sore throat* include a slight tingling in the back of the throat that is especially noticeable when the child swallows, followed by the appearance of pain one or two days later. Pain may occur with other symptoms of a cold. The lymph glands in the neck may also become swollen.

In a minority of cases, bacteria, especially the *streptococcus* baccilli, begin to develop. These infections are commonly referred to as "strep throat." When bacteria develop, the symptoms generally appear more rapidly. Children may develop a high fever, pain in the throat, and swollen glands in several hours. Other symptoms of a cold may or may not be present.

In general, viruses are more yin, while bacteria are more yang. Antibiotics, which are extremely yin, are effective in neutralizing more yang bacteria, but have no effect on more yin viruses. Yin and yang attract and neutralize each other, while yin and yin repel. However, antibiotics do not address the underlying cause.

Laryngitis, or inflammation of the voice box, may occur together with a cold. The inflammation is usually a virus type and disappears within forty-eight hours. *Croup* is a more severe form of laryngitis, in which the inflamed larynx blocks the normal passage of air. Croup usually appears in the evening, when the lungs and respiratory passages become more active in discharging mucus and other excessive factors. The symptoms of croup include difficulty in breathing, and a hard, ringing cough. A child with croup will often suck in the chest with each breath and make a strange noise that sounds like barking.

The *tonsils* are small, oval bodies located at the top of the throat on either side. The adenoids are located in the upper part of the throat. They are both part of the lymphatic system and are frequent sites for the localization of excess. *Tonsillitis* is the enlargement and inflammation of the tonsils as a result of the accumulation of excess. When inflammation occurs in the adenoids, the condition is known as *adenoiditis.*

It is not uncommon for children who eat the modern diet to regularly experience both conditions. Many children have three or four episodes of tonsillitis per year.

The tonsils play an important role in natural immunity. When excess accumulates in the body, the tonsils and adenoids help localize it. They also localize viruses and bacteria, and this is why they become inflamed.

Tonsillitis and adenoiditis are rare in children who do not consume dairy products, sugar, tropical fruits, and meat, eggs, and other animal products containing saturated fats. The underlying cause of these conditions is the extremes in diet that produce excess in the blood and lymph streams and throughout the body.

Removing the tonsils does not solve the underlying problem. What it does do is weaken the person's overall vitality and ability to resist infection.

At one time, removal of the tonsils was almost routine. More than a million and a half *tonsillectomies* were performed every year during the 1930s. However, in the face of growing criticism, the number of yearly operations has dropped by about two-thirds.

The relationship between these lymphatic tissues and the body as a whole can be understood when we consider their embryonic origins. The glands that develop in the throat share a similar structure and quality to the reproductive organs. The uvula at the back of the throat is similar in structure and quality to the penis and the clitoris. These organs receive a strong external charge from heaven's more yang, descending force. The uvula is surrounded on either side by the adenoids. The penis is surrounded by the testes. The adenoids and testes are similar in structure and quality.

The tongue is charged primarily by an opposite quality of energy—the expanding energy of the earth—and its structure and quality are very similar to the vagina. The ovaries also receive an external charge primarily from the earth, and their quality is similar to the tonsils.

Inflammation of the tonsils and adenoids is an indication that the overall condition of the body has become imbalanced. The reproductive organs, in particular, have become weaker. The wide incidence of tonsillitis and adenoiditis over the last several generations corresponds to the large number of reproductive disorders, including infertility, that are being reported today.

Sexual vitality and reproductive ability are further weakened when the tonsils and adenoids are removed. As a consequence, these operations are contributing to the modern increase in sexual frustration, unhappiness, and disorders, and to the decline in fertility and reproductive ability.

Removing the tonsils and adenoids does not solve the underlying problem that causes inflammation and enlargement in these areas. When these organs are removed, other lymphatic organs must take over their function. People who have had their tonsils and adenoids taken out have less resistance to toxic excess, and are also less able to eliminate excess than are people who still have these organs intact. Because they are more susceptible to illness, individuals who have had these organs removed need to eat well throughout life.

The symptoms of tonsillitis may include high fever, vomiting, headache, and a general feeling of malaise. The tonsils become red and swollen, and tiny white spots or larger patches of white pus may develop. Pain in the throat is usually more severe in older children.

Excess may also accumulate in other lymph glands in the neck, causing them to become enlarged and infected. Enlargement of glands may also occur after the tonsillitis (or other throat infection) has subsided, and may last for weeks.

The use of antibiotics to treat throat infections, including tonsillitis, is now being questioned. Antibiotics are recommended in cases where the streptococcus bacteria is found. The primary reason for using antibiotics is to prevent the infection from leading to more serious consequences, including rheumatic fever and inflammation of the kidneys. However, most sore throats do not involve streptococcus, while the possibility of rheumatic fever, even when streptococcus is present, is normally very slight. *Rheumatic fever,* a more yin condition, is rarely seen among adequately nourished children. It occurs among children who receive a chronically unbalanced diet, for example, diets lacking in whole grains, fresh vegetables, and other complex carbohydrate foods, and diets that lack a wide enough variety and selection of foods. The intake of simple sugar, including soft drinks, refined, white bread or flour, poor quality oils or fats, and highly acidic vegetables such as potatoes and tomatoes also contributes to this condition. These imbalances weaken the natural immunity and can allow bacteria to flourish.

It is important to note that many children have streptococcus bacteria in their throats yet do not develop an infection. Infections result when the natural immunity is compromised through an inadequate diet.

General Adjustments in Diet: When children experience a sore throat, parents need to assess their overall condition, including their diet and activity, so as to discover the underlying cause. As with the other common conditions that affect children, the underlying cause of a throat discharge could be the repeated intake of more excessive foods—such as too much fruit or juice, oily snacks, or simple sugars—or from the one-time intake of some extremely imbalanced food, such as birthday cake made with sugar or ice cream. Like other common discharges, sore throats normally clear up once the excessive factors have been eliminated from the body. However, if the child continues to eat more extreme foods as a regular part of the diet, sore throats and infections normally recur with regularity.

Therefore, the most fundamental way to eliminate sore throats is to avoid extreme or excessive foods and beverages. The intake of sugar and concentrated sweeteners, oily or greasy foods, spices, tropical fruits, iced or chilled beverages, and poor quality fats and oils is best reduced or avoided. Children can eat according to the standard macrobiotic diet, with the appropriate adjustments for their age and condition.

The adjustments in daily diet presented earlier for colds and flu can also be applied in cases of sore throat. If children have difficulty in swallowing, their grain, vegetable, bean, and other dishes can be cooked with more water and mashed into semi-solids in a suribachi or baby food mill.

Special Dishes and Home Care: Special preparations for sore throats are similar to those for colds, flu, or fevers. If the air in a heated home or apartment is especially dry, the atmosphere in the child's room can be kept moist with any of the methods described in the section on home care for colds or flu.

In addition, any of the home care applications presented earlier for related symptoms including fever, headache, or general fatigue may also be applied in cases of sore throat. In many instances, a mild sore throat develops together with other symptoms of a cold or flu.

For tonsillitis or other throat inflammations, cool applications are often helpful. You may apply either cold towels, a mashed greens (chlorophyll) plaster, a tofu/chlorophyll plaster, or a mashed tofu plaster. Instructions for preparing these applications are presented in the *Recipe and Home Care Guide.*

Palm Healing: Palm healing can also help ease the discomfort of a sore throat. To apply palm healing, have the child sit in a relaxed posture. The child can also lie comfortably on the back. Place one hand gently across the upper part of the neck, immediately under the lower jaw. Place the other hand opposite to this on the back of the neck. Breathe quietly and gently and apply the hands for 15 to 20 minutes before detaching them.

If the child is experiencing other discomforting symptoms, any of the methods described earlier may also be used.

Measles

In the macrobiotic view, measles is not an illness in the usual sense of the word. Rather, it is a natural discharge of unnecessary factors accumulated in the womb. Through the measles, a baby discharges some of the yang quality that remains from the embryonic period.

At one time, measles was a common childhood disorder. Practically every child experienced it. Now, however, it is relatively rare for a child to have the measles.

There are several possible reasons for this decline in incidence. The first is the widespread use of mass-produced, chemicalized, artificial foods, many of which are extremely yin. Items such as ice cream, sugared cereals and sweets, soft drinks, processed fruit juices, cow's milk, and artificial infant formulas weaken a child's ability to discharge effectively. When children eat a large volume of these and other modern foods, or if they are consumed during pregnancy, the child's capacity for discharging excess, including the measles, is diminished. Another factor that inhibits discharging abilities is the use of the measles vaccine. The vaccine has the potential to cause many serious complications, and stimulates the production of antibodies that interfere with the natural discharge of the measles.

If a normally healthy child with measles is cared for properly by parents, the risk of complications is slight. It is actually beneficial for children to discharge excessive factors in the form of measles. The attempt to prevent measles through vaccination could cause excess to be stored deep within the body, contributing to more serious degenerative conditions in the future. The incidence of measles started to decline before the vaccine was widely introduced. This was due largely to the shift from a more natural to a more artificially processed diet, and the corresponding decline in natural discharging power. However, many children who receive the vaccine develop measles anyway, indicating that the vaccine is frequently ineffective.

The first symptoms of measles are often similar to those of a cold. Red, watery eyes, fatigue, loss of appetite, and a dry cough are common. A fever starts to develop, usually becoming higher with each passing day. A rash usually appears within three or four days, in the form of faint pink dots on the head and neck. It eventually spreads over the whole body, during which time fever and coughing normally continue. The temperature often returns to normal once the rash reaches the feet.

Special dishes or external applications—including those for reducing fevers—are usually not used as a part of the macrobiotic approach to measles. It is better not to interfere with the natural discharge. Provided no serious complications arise, it is far wiser to encourage it to come out. The rash and fever indicate that a child's discharging abilities are functioning normally.

It is important for a child with measles to eat as simply and cleanly as possible, avoiding extremes that could prolong the discharge or increase the likelihood of complications. Children with measles can generally eat according to the standard macrobiotic diet, with appropriate adjustments for age and physical makeup. The special dietary modifications for colds and flu, such as making daily foods with a softer consistency, may also be tried.

In normal circumstances, do not apply mashed tofu or chlorophyll plasters or prepare any of the daikon or other special teas that are often used to naturally reduce a fever. The discharge of measles can be gently and naturally encouraged to come out by utilizing the following simple home care adjustments.

1. Let the child rest quietly in his room. Pull the shades down or close the curtains to darken the room slightly.
2. Moisten the air by placing one or two pots of steaming water in the child's room. Humidifiers or electric steam vaporizers may also be used, or moist towels may be placed on radiators.
3. Keep the child comfortably warm. Windows can normally be kept closed. However, open them slightly from time to time to allow fresh air to circulate when the weather is warm.
4. Keep the child indoors. If children go outside in the fresh air and sunshine before the discharge is complete, excess may be driven inside toward the internal organs. A high fever or some other type of discharge may occur later, or complications such as pneumonia could arise. It is better to keep the child indoors for about a week after the measles appear to be over so as to allow the discharge to fully run its course.

If, however, the fever becomes dangerously high—above 104°F.—some measures should be employed to lower it. A chlorophyll plaster made from finely chopped, mashed greens can be applied for a short while until the temperature begins to drop.

Parents need not fear the measles. With the proper dietary and lifestyle approach, children shed their embryonic excess smoothly and begin a new stage of growth and development. (For further information about measles, including a discussion of complications that occur in rare cases, refer to *Macrobiotic Pregnancy and Care of the Newborn*.) Parents who suspect complications are advised to seek the appropriate medical care.

Roseola

Unlike measles, *roseola* (which is sometimes referred to as "one-day measles") is not necessary for further growth and development. It is more of a conditional problem caused by excesses in the diet, especially the overconsumption of more extreme yin items such as sugar, soft drinks, ice cream, and tropical fruits, together with fats and oils, including those in milk and other dairy products, eggs, meat, poultry, and other animal foods.

When children eat a more centrally balanced diet, they usually do not develop roseola. Since the symptoms of roseola often resemble those of the measles, if your child has not yet had the measles, it is generally better not to do anything to reduce the fever and to deal with the condition as if it were the measles.

However, in roseola, the fever may come on suddenly and rapidly rise to 103°F. to 105°F. Some children experience convulsions, known as *febrile seizures*, as a result of this sudden rise in temperature. If the fever climbs above 103°F. to 104°F., the chlorophyll plaster described in the discussion of measles can be applied for a short time until the temperature begins to go down. The fever may last three to four days, after which a rash appears, usually covering the whole body except for the face and legs. The rash usually lasts for 24 hours.

In general, children with roseola can rest in bed until they feel well enough to be up and about. However, it is better to wait until you are sure they do not have the measles before letting them go outside. Children with roseola can eat according to the standard macrobiotic diet, with emphasis on any of the more simple foods that they prefer. The home care approaches for measles can be generally applied for roseola, until you are sure that the child does not have the measles. At that time, the child can simply rest at home until he or she recovers.

Mumps

Unlike measles, which represents a natural constitutional discharge, *mumps* comes about when a child discharges excessive factors that were eaten after birth or later in childhood. Mumps is very common among children who eat the modern diet, but occurs much more rarely among children who eat a naturally balanced diet. A primary cause of mumps is the overconsumption of more extreme yin foods and drinks, including ice cream, candy, sugared soft drinks, artificial sweeteners, tropical fruits, acidic vegetables such as potatoes and tomatoes, spices, and oily or greasy foods. Mumps may develop suddenly after a child goes to a party or social gathering and eats foods such as cake, ice cream, chips, or soda.

Mumps represents the accumulation and discharge of excess in the throat, particularly in and around the salivary glands. There are several sets of salivary glands in the throat and among them, a particular set of glands, known as the *parotids*, are most commonly affected. In the majority of cases, the swelling is located on one side of the throat, although the glands on the other side of the throat may also begin to swell.

Aside from swollen glands, the other symptoms of mumps include headache, loss of appetite, and a mild fever. The symptoms normally last for about a week, or until the excessive factors that the body seeks to eliminate are discharged.

At present, it is believed that mumps is caused by a virus. However, not everyone who is exposed to the virus develops the condition. Some exposed people develop a very mild, or *subclinical*, form of the illness, some develop full-blown mumps, while others are not affected at all. Therefore, the underlying cause of mumps is not a virus but imbalance in the daily diet that leads to abnormal discharge and susceptibility to the virus.

Modern medicine has now developed a mumps vaccine. The vaccine is sometimes given routinely to children. The vaccine suppresses the body's ability to discharge toxins and does not correct the underlying imbalances that produce susceptibility to mumps. Suppressing a discharge such as mumps can result in toxic excess being held inside the body where it can lead to another form of discharge or to eventual deterioration and weakening of the internal organs. The vaccine could actually contribute to development of a degenerative condition later in life.

General Adjustments in Diet: Children with mumps can eat according to the standard macrobiotic diet, with appropriate adjustments for their age and condition. It is important for children to avoid extremely yin items that could aggravate the condition, including sugar, ice cream, milk, soft drinks, and tropical fruits. If necessary, the child's food can be prepared with more water as described in the section on colds and flu. Since the condition is caused largely by the overconsumption of more yin foods and beverages, it is important for the child to limit or avoid intake of fruit, fruit juice, carbonated beverages, oil, flour products (which can cause stagnation in the intestines), chips and other snack foods, oil, nut butters, and concentrated sweeteners. We recommend using cooked or dried fruits, rather than fresh fruits or juices, and limiting the intake of concentrated sweeteners to an occasional small volume of rice syrup or barley malt until the child recovers. Children can also enjoy moderate consumption of bancha tea, cereal grain teas, or other macrobiotic beverages.

Special Dishes and Preparations: The fever of mumps is usually not very high. If it does become uncomfortably high, however, any of the special macrobiotic drinks presented in the section on fever may be used, with appropriate considerations for the age and overall condition of the child. If loss of appetite occurs, special rice cream or soft brown rice may be given daily until it returns to normal. A mild ume-sho-kuzu drink, given once a day for several days, helps neutralize an overly acidic blood condition and strengthens the digestion. The drink should be milder than that taken by adults and should not be given to children who have not yet begun to use salt. Very mildly seasoned carrot and burdock *kinpira*, prepared without oil, can be included along with other vegetable dishes every couple of days for a week or so until the child regains normal strength.

Home Care: Unless the child complains of fever, or unless the fever becomes uncomfortably high, home applications such as the tofu plaster need not be used. However, if the fever becomes uncomfortably high, the external applications presented earlier in the section on fever may be used.

For the swelling in the throat, a tofu/chlorophyll plaster or any of the cool applications recommended for tonsillitis may be applied to the throat. It can be employed several times a day for several days until the swelling is reduced. Leave each application in place for about an hour before removing it or replacing it with a fresh plaster.

If the child complains of a headache, the applications presented in the discussion of headache can be used, depending upon the location of the pain.

The child with mumps can rest or play at home until the swelling returns to normal and strength and appetite are regained.

Palm Healing: A variety of palm healing techniques can be used to ease discomfort. For pain and discomfort in the throat, the technique described in the section on sore throats and tonsillitis may be used. The techniques used for headaches and fever may also be applied if necessary.

Chicken Pox

Chicken pox is a common childhood illness, although many macrobiotic children never experience it. When the child's intake includes many fatty or oily items, including milk, chicken, eggs, pizza, fried foods, and chips, or too many simple sugars, including those in fruit, refined sugar, and concentrated sweeteners, the excessive factors contained in these foods may erupt in a skin discharge. The discharge is thought to be triggered by a virus. However, not everyone who is exposed to the virus develops chicken pox. Some exposed children develop a very mild form of the illness with only a few blisters, others develop a rash and blisters over the entire body. These differences in susceptibility are due to differences in diet, physical constitution, and environment.

The main symptoms of chicken pox include low grade fever, aches and pains, and a loss of appetite. As the blisters turn to scabs, the child often experiences itching. The scabs usually peel off within ten days or so.

General Adjustments in Diet: Children with chicken pox may eat according to the standard macrobiotic diet, with appropriate adjustments for their age and condition.

During the time that the chicken pox is coming in, it is better not to serve animal food to the child. However, a small piece of broiled white-meat fish may be eaten on occasion if craved, together with a garnish of one or two tablespoons of grated raw daikon and one or two drops of tamari. It is better for the child to avoid buckwheat groats, soba noodles, or buckwheat flour. Salad, raw fruit, and fruit juices are best minimized or avoided until the condition clears up. It is also better to reduce or avoid bread, muffins, cookies, pancakes, or other flour products; however, whole wheat noodles or unleavened sourdough bread may be eaten occasionally. The intake of sweets is best limited to occasional cooked fruit dessert, while the use of oil is best minimized or avoided, as are nuts and nut butters. The child can enjoy lightly toasted sesame seeds sprinkled on various dishes, and other roasted seeds can be eaten as snacks.

The child can return to the standard macrobiotic diet appropriate for his or her age and condition once the condition clears up.

Special Dishes and Preparations:
1. *For aches and pains*—A mild ume-sho-kuzu drink may be given once a day for several days. The drink should be mildly seasoned—much more mildly than for adults—and children who have not yet begun to include salt should not be given it. It is also helpful for headaches.
3. *For lack of appetite*—Children can take one or two bowls of *special rice cream* each day for several days, in addition to their other grains and normal dishes. A small volume of macrobiotic condiments may be used when appropriate.

Home Care: Children with chicken pox can rest at home as they recover. The condition can spread to other susceptible children for about two weeks after the rash comes in. Children can be kept at home during this period.

For itching—A warm daily nuka (rice bran) bath can help relieve itching. The child can soak in hot nuka water for several minutes daily, or a towel or facecloth can be dipped in warm nuka water and used to pat the affected area. A skin wash can also be made with dried daikon or turnip leaves. See the section on skin disorders for instructions.

Itching often becomes worse when wool or synthetic fibers are used for clothing or sheets, pillowcases, or blankets. Cotton pajamas, underwear, bathrobes, and bedding are preferable to synthetics to minimize itching. Soaps and shampoos made from natural vegetable quality materials are also preferable to those containing chemicals.

Palm Healing: Palm healing can be used to ease the discomfort of headaches, fever or other symptoms. Please refer to the appropriate sections for suggested methods.

Whooping Cough

Whooping cough is known in the Orient as "100 days cough." Whooping cough, or *pertussis* as it is known medically, is a form of discharge. Susceptible individuals may develop whooping cough after exposure to pertussis bacteria. The severity of the illness varies, from a light cough and mild symptoms to severe coughing with a whooping sound on each inhalation. Children with a more severe form of the disease sometimes cough repeatedly with every breath, and their faces may turn blue or purplish in color. Choking and vomiting may accompany severe coughing. Whooping cough can last for more than three months; hence the name "100 days cough." Children with healthy autoimmune systems resulting from a naturally balanced diet normally do not experience this condition.

The underlying dietary cause of whooping cough is the overconsumption of more extreme yin foods, including sugar, honey, tropical fruits, juices, carbonated beverages and refined flour products, along with fats such as those found in milk and other dairy products. People of all ages develop whooping cough, but more than half of those who do are under two. In cases where newborns or young children are afflicted, the primary dietary cause is the type of food eaten by the mother during pregnancy or the use of cow's milk or artificial formulas following birth.

When infants develop the condition, it is recommended that medical advice be sought, due to the possibility of complications including pneumonia. Children with severe coughing are also best referred to appropriate medical care.

There is presently a great deal of controversy surrounding the immunization given for pertussis, much of it within the medical community. It is given as part of the *DPT* (diphtheria, pertussis, tetanus) inoculation. The vaccine has the potential to cause damaging side effects and in many cases has been found to be ineffective in preventing the disease. In his book, *How to Raise a Healthy Child in Spite of Your Doctor*, Dr. Robert S. Mendelsohn suggests pertussis had already begun to decline before the vaccine came into use.* The most frequently noted side effects of the vaccine include fever, crying, emotional upset, swelling, soreness, and redness in the area of the injection. More serious side effects have also been reported, including convulsions and brain damage. Some researchers have begun to suspect a connection between the vaccine and *Sudden Infant Death Syndrome* (SIDS).

General Adjustments in Diet: A child with whooping cough can eat according to the standard macrobiotic diet, with appropriate adjustments for age and condition. (In cases where a nursing infant develops whooping cough, it is recommended that the mother avoid extremes and eat according to the standard macrobiotic diet appropriate to her needs.) In general, more yin extremes, including sugar, tropical fruits and juices, ice cream, spices, soft drinks, and milk and milk products are best avoided. Even within the standard diet, a child with this condition must be careful not to overindulge in fruit, especially raw fruit or juice, salad, concentrated sweeteners, and oily or greasy snacks.

Brown rice may serve as the principal grain. When desired, it may be served softly cooked or in soups. Other grains may be used regularly as supplements to brown rice. Children may also take a cup or two of special rice cream from time to time. An appropriate volume of condiments may also be eaten with grain dishes. Lotus root seeds, which can be beneficial to the lungs and respiratory passages, may be added to brown rice three or four times per week. Add 15 to 20 percent soaked lotus seeds to your brown rice prior to cooking. Light miso or tamari broth soups may also be served when appropriate.

Root vegetables, cooked along with their green tops, can also be helpful in relieving lung problems. Daikon and their greens, or carrot and turnip and their tops can be served often, along with other vegetable dishes. Root vegetables and

* Readers are referred to this book for an excellent discussion of the problems related to immunization in general.

their green tops are especially nourishing for the lungs and their complementary partner, the large intestine. Lightly boiled salad or quickly steamed greens are preferable to raw salad during recovery. Lotus root—either fresh or dried—may also be included in vegetable or sea vegetable dishes or in soups.

A small piece of white-meat fish may be eaten on occasion if desired by older children. It is better to limit the intake of fruit to occasional small servings of cooked northern fruit. Concentrated sweeteners are best reduced or avoided during recovery, as are nuts and nut butters.

Brown rice tea may be used alternately with bancha and other macrobiotic beverages. It is recommended that all beverages be served hot or room temperature. The child may return to the appropriate standard macrobiotic diet once the condition returns to normal.

Special Dishes and Preparations: Any of the dishes and teas presented in the section on colds and flu may be given when appropriate. Lotus root tea, which is described in that section, can be especially helpful in easing chest congestion and coughing.

Home Care: Children with whopping cough can rest at home and, when necessary, in bed. Because of concern for the possibility of spreading the illness, children are often kept at home for five weeks after the beginning of the sickness. If children have no fever and feel up to it, they can play outside for short periods, provided they are properly dressed to prevent chilling. The air in the child's room can be kept slightly cooler than normal, and windows can be opened to allow cool air to circulate. Again, make sure that the child is properly dressed and covered. Any of the home care applications presented in the section on colds and flu can be applied to ease discomforting symptoms. Warm towels to the chest or a warm towel body rub can be especially helpful. Hot or warm towels should not be given during a fever.

Palm Healing: Palm healing can be used to ease discomfort in the lungs and chest region. Any of the following methods can be used:

1. *Applying the palm to the front of the chest.*   This application can be done with the child lying comfortably on the back. Place one hand gently over the chest, covering both lungs. Breathe with a normal rhythm, and detach the hand after 15 to 20 minutes. The sound of "Su" may be added on the exhalation.
2. *Applying palms to the chest and upper back.*   This application can be done with the child sitting up. Place one hand on the chest, covering the region of the lungs. Place the other palm opposite on the upper back. Breathe and continue as above.
3. *Applying palms and fingers to the lungs and lung meridian.*   The lung meridian runs down along the inside of both arms to the thumbs. To treat both

Figure 14 Applying Palms to the Chest and Upper Back

regions, have the child lie comfortably on the back. Sit on either side of the child. Gently hold one of the child's thumbs between the thumb and index finger and place the other palm lightly over the chest. Breathe and continue as above for 10 to 12 minutes. After applying the hands in the above manner, sit on the other side of the child and gently hold the opposite thumb with one hand and place the other on the chest. Breathe and continue as above for 10 to 12 minutes before detaching the hands.

Orthopedic Problems, Including Rickets

Many common bone and joint problems correct themselves when appropriate adjustments are made in a child's diet and activity. The most common orthopedic problems can be classified into two broad categories: those caused by an excess of more yin items in the diet, and those caused by an excess of more yang items. A lack of balance in the child's daily environment can also produce developmental problems, as the development of rickets illustrates.

More yin orthopedic problems include *bowed legs, pigeon toes* (toeing in), *flat feet, pigeon chest*—in which the breastbone and front of the chest are pushed outward—*congenital hip displacement*, and *scoliosis* in which the spine curves outward. More yang orthopedic problems include *knock-knees* and *funnel chest*—in which the breastbone and front of the chest are pushed inward. Orthopedic problems caused by the combined effects of both extremes include *lateral scoliosis*—in which the spine curves to the left or right, *rickets*, and *wryneck*, or *torticollis*.

More yin conditions can result from overconsumption of fruit—especially tropical fruit—sugar and other concentrated sweeteners, fluids, milk, ice cream, soy milk, tofu, soft drinks, and oily snacks. Too many watery foods and flour products may also contribute to more yin conditions, as can overeating. Overly yang conditions can result from overconsumption of meat, eggs, fish, or other forms of animal protein, salt, and baked foods. A lack of variety, for example, not enough fresh or lightly cooked vegetables, or an overly restricted diet can also produce more yang developmental problems. Conditions that result from the combination of both extremes are often caused by the overintake of sugar, milk, fruits, and other more yin items, plus meat, animal food, salt, and baked foods. A lack of variety can also contribute to the development of these problems.

General Adjustments in Diet: As mentioned above, minor orthopedic problems often improve with time and the practice of a balanced natural diet. When a specific imbalance is found to exist, minor dietary adjustments can often help correct it. Conditions caused by overeating or by the intake of too many yin items can be improved when the overall volume of food is kept moderate and the intake of more yin extremes is reduced or stopped. Within the standard diet, too many fruits, juices, concentrated sweeteners, oily snacks, or overly watery dishes can interfere with recovery. The regular intake of soy milk, which contains plenty of fat, can also interfere.

More yang developmental problems can be improved when the child is offered more variety in the diet, including a variety of whole grains, a wide selection of vegetables—including those which are lightly cooked such as quick, steamed greens and boiled salad—and the normally wide range of foods and cooking methods within standard macrobiotic practice. If a child becomes overly contracted, be especially careful about the intake of salt and baked flour products, including bread, muffins, chips, and crackers.

When children have an imbalanced condition caused by both extremes, a centrally balanced diet—with plenty of variety in the selection of foods and cooking methods—would be appropriate. Extremes of yin or yang are best minimized or avoided.

Of course, in every case, the standard macrobiotic approach must be adapted to suit the child's age and condition.

Home Care: Daily life considerations are also important. Appropriate exercise and outdoor play—with frequent exposure to sunlight—helps a child maintain a healthy balance. *Rickets*, for example, results largely from a lack of sunshine. Ultraviolet radiation from the sun is needed by the body for the production of *calciferol*, a hormone that promotes normal calcification in the bones. If the body does not produce enough calciferol, a variety of bone deformities occur. Severely affected children may develop thickened joints, deformed legs, an enlarged head, and spinal deformities.

Rickets is often thought of as a disease of industrial civilization. The earliest cases were reported in England in the mid-1600s, at about the time that the burning of soft coal began to become widespread, thickening the atmosphere and blocking the sun's rays. It was also around that time that people started living in dark, narrow streets within the larger cities. By 1889, the British Medical Association found rickets to be most prevalent in "large towns and thickly peopled districts, especially where industrial pursuits are carried on." Very few cases were found in the countryside.

In the late 1800s, a British medical missionary by the name of Theobald Palms visited Japan. He noted an "absence of rickets among the Japanese as compared with its lamentable frequency among the poor children of the large centers of population in England and Scotland." The traditional Japanese diet at that time consisted largely of brown rice and other whole grains, sea vegetables, beans and soy products, and occasional fish. However, Japan enjoys a bright, sunny climate, in comparison to the more overcast climate of northern Europe. Japanese children also spent a great deal of time out of doors, even in winter.

If children eat a well-balanced macrobiotic diet—with ample variety—and are taken outside on a regular basis, preferably everyday, we need not worry about rickets. Children who have a tendency toward this disorder can include regular servings of fish in their diets. Special efforts must also be made to encourage them to play outside in the sunshine. In addition to the appropriate standard macrobiotic diet—with a wide range of foods and cooking methods, including regular servings of cooked white-meat fish—children with more serious conditions may require fish-liver oils as dietary supplements. It is recommended that children with more serious conditions also consult with a physician in addition to employing macrobiotic suggestions.

Scrubbing the body daily with a warm moist towel is also beneficial for developmental problems. Special care can be given to the areas of the body—for example, the legs or along the spine—where the main problem exists. A towel that is dipped in warm ginger water can also be used for body scrubbing from time to time.

If a child is experiencing pain, parents can apply either warm towel compresses or palm healing directly to the painful region. Place your palm lightly on the affected area for 15 to 20 minutes. Breathe as described in previous sections. Warm, moist towels can be applied repeatedly to the painful area for 5 to 10 minutes.

Supplementary approaches—including acupuncture, shiatsu massage, and physical therapy can also be helpful in some cases. It is recommended that children with more serious developmental disabilities be referred to the appropriate medical professional, in addition to applying the general dietary and lifestyle modifications presented above.

Bed-wetting and Sleeping Difficulties

There are many varieties of bed-wetting, the medical term for which is *enuresis*. In one variety, a child does not develop nighttime bladder control. In another, a child develops control but lapses into periods of wetting the bed.

It is commonly thought that bed-wetting is caused largely by emotional or psychological problems. Although these certainly play a role in many cases, dietary imbalances are often the more direct, underlying cause.

The two main types of bed-wetting have opposite dietary causes. Some children consistently release urine early in the evening, soon after going to sleep. Others wet the bed later at night or early in the morning.

In the early evening, atmospheric energy is becoming more still or quiet. We may say that it is settling down. If a child eats too many yin foods, he or she will be more likely to wet the bed early in the evening, when atmospheric energy is more contractive. An overly expanded bladder releases urine so as to contract along with the energy of the environment.

The overintake of more yin foods or beverages can also interfere with sound sleep during the early evening. When a child has difficulty in going to sleep, or tends to wake up soon after going to bed, the cause is often the overintake of more excessive yin items. An overly yin condition prevents the child from "settling down' into a deep and restful sleep.

The earth's atmosphere begins to "awaken" in the early morning. Energy begins to move in an upward direction. The bladder normally expands and relaxes at this time, as urine accumulates in it. When children wet their beds in the early morning—say, from 2:00 to 7:00 A.M.—the cause is often the overintake of salt or other excessively yang items. These can cause the bladder to become chronically tight and constricted, and limit its capacity to hold urine. Excess can then easily spill over in the form of bed-wetting.

A more yang imbalance can cause a child to have difficulty in sleeping during the early morning hours. The child can easily become restless and unsettled during this time if the diet contains too many excessively yang factors.

When the bladder is overly expanded, the intake of more excessively yin foods and beverages can be reduced or avoided. Fruit and fruit juice, sugar and concentrated sweeteners, too many salads or raw vegetables, spices, or too much fluid contribute to this condition.

However, do not overcompensate by trying to give the child too many salty foods. The use of salt should at all times be appropriate for the child's age and condition. A generally balanced macrobiotic diet with appropriate variety would be most beneficial. Simply be careful about the intake of too many fruits, concentrated sweeteners, salads, or fluids.

For an overly contracted condition, reduce or avoid the intake of excessively yang items. Meat, eggs, and poultry are best avoided, and white-meat fish is recommended for occasional consumption only. Within the appropriate macrobiotic diet, be careful about the intake of salt and baked flour products, and be sure that the child enjoys plenty of lightly steamed or boiled vegetables. High quality yin items—such as hot apple cider, baked apples, or cooked northern fruits can often help relax the bladder when taken on occasion.

These recommendations may also be applied when children have trouble sleeping, depending on whether the child wakes up earlier or later in the evening.

Pinworms

Pinworms are the most common type of worms affecting children. They look like tiny pieces of white thread and live in the large intestine. They migrate through the colon and come out at night through the rectum to lay eggs. They can often be found at night between the buttocks or in the child's bowel movements. The most common symptom is itching that becomes more noticeable at night.

Some of the other symptoms of pinworms (and other varieties of worms) include:

1. Fatigue or laziness.
2. Cravings for certain foods or a feeling of unsatisfied hunger. Children with worms sometimes stay thin even when they are eating a great deal.
3. Irritability, short temper, and crying. Children with worms may suddenly become hysterical without any apparent reason.
4. Periodic anemia.
5. Occasional nausea or stomach pain arising an hour or so after eating.
6. Nail biting.
7. A consistently loose or fragmented bowel movement.
8. Tiny pinpoint indentations in the fingernails.

Children with worms can begin the standard macrobiotic diet, with appropriate considerations for their age and condition. It is recommended that raw fruits, nuts, or raw vegetables be reduced temporarily or sometimes avoided until the condition improves. Children who are old enough can eat several pieces of mochi everyday for several weeks along with *soba* (buckwheat noodles) several times per week. Various types of seeds can also help improve the condition. Pumpkin, squash, or sunflower seeds can be lightly roasted without salt and given as snacks or over rice or other dishes.

In addition to their regular beverages, children with worms can also be given mild *Corsican* sea vegetable tea. A cup or two can be taken daily in addition to their usual beverages for a week or so. (Please see the *Recipe and Home Care Guide* for suggestions for preparing this tea.) Corsican sea vegetable is available in many natural food stores.

The soreness and itching produced by pinworms can often be relieved by applying a mixture of sesame oil and a pinch of freshly grated ginger directly to the anus. Use a piece of sanitized cotton to apply it, and follow the application with a warm towel.

If macrobiotic children develop worms, the cause is often the overintake of oily, fatty, or floury foods. Keeping the intake of these items to a minimum helps prevent worms. Cleanliness is also helpful in preventing the spread of worms. Make sure children wash their hands after going to the toilet and keep their nails properly cleaned and trimmed.

Unlike the medications given to control worms, these natural approaches do not produce undesirable side effects or disrupt the child's overall condition.

Skin Disorders

The skin is one of the major pathways for the discharge of excess. When excess accumulates in the bloodstream, the body may discharge it in the form of a skin disease.

The more common conditions that affect the skin include: *prickly heat, eczema,* and *diaper rash*, as well as *scabies, impetigo,* and *ringworm*. Some children also experience *poison ivy, warts,* and *head lice*. The underlying dietary factors that promote these conditions are presented below. (For a discussion of skin problems in the newborn, including diaper rash, cradle cap and birthmarks, refer to *Macrobiotic Pregnancy and Care of the Newborn*.)

1. *Prickly Heat*—Prickly heat occurs with babies, often in hot weather. The underlying dietary cause includes overconsumption of simple sugars, in combination with oils and fats, including those in dairy products. These items cause fat and oil to accumulate in the sweat glands leading to blockage and inflammation. The condition usually becomes worse when the weather is hot and the child perspires. It can also result when a mother consumes too many of these foods while nursing.

2. *Eczema*—The underlying dietary causes of eczema are similar to those of prickly heat: specifically, the overconsumption of fats and oils, including those in milk and other dairy products, animal foods, and vegetable oils. The overintake of simple sugars, including those in refined sugar, corn syrup, honey, and fruits is often a contributing cause. The overintake of baked flour products can also contribute to eczema and other skin conditions.

Eczema takes the form of a rash with patches of red, rough skin. The rash tends to occur on certain areas of the body; for example, babies are often affected on the cheeks, while in older children, it often appears behind the knees or in the folds of the elbows, or on the forearms and neck. The location of the rash shows which of the internal organs is being primarily affected by accumulations of mucus and fat. The cheeks, for example, reflect the condition of the lungs. Eczema on the cheeks shows that mucus is accumulating there. Eczema on the arms and legs normally occurs along the meridians, and reveals dysfunction in the corresponding organs and functions. Eczema on the front or back of the body frequently reflects dysfunction in the organs located in the same general area. The condition is often chronic and produces itching. When children continually scratch the area, the skin may become hard and thick. Children with eczema also have a tendency to develop asthma and allergies, both of which are frequently caused by the overconsumption of milk, dairy products, and other more yin items.

3. *Scabies*—Scabies are clusters of pimples that develop scabs. They can cause severe itching, and children frequently scratch them to the point that these scabs break open. They are caused primarily by the overconsumption of animal fats and oils—including those in milk and dairy products—and simple sugars such as those

in concentrated sweeteners and tropical fruits. The location of scabies correlates with the internal organs that are primarily affected.

4. *Impetigo*—The overconsumption of animal fats, especially those in poultry, cheese, and eggs, is the primary cause of impetigo. Too many oily or greasy dishes, even those prepared with vegetable oils—including French fries and chips—also contribute, as does the overintake of simple sugars. The main symptom in older children is scabs or crusty skin with a brownish-yellow color. These markings often start on the face and spread elsewhere. In infants, the condition usually takes the form of small blisters with yellowish fluid and pus. The blisters usually break and leave an exposed raw sore.

5. *Poison Ivy*—Exposure to poison ivy (or such plants as *poison oak* or *sumac*) can trigger a skin eruption. The rash usually develops within two days after contact with the leaves of the plant. As it develops, the skin becomes red, swollen, and clusters of small blisters appear. The rash normally disappears in two to three weeks. It usually causes itching and burning. The irritation is caused by a chemical, *oleoresin*, found in the leaves, stems, and roots of the plant.

The overintake of sugar, fruit—especially tropical varieties—soft drinks, juices, milk, spices and highly acidic vegetables make the skin more susceptible to poison ivy, and can make the symptoms more severe.

6. *Warts*—Warts represent the discharge of excess. The most common cause is the overconsumption of animal protein. Many people experience the disappearance of warts once they reduce their intake of animal products. Warts are often located along meridians that correspond to internal organs.

7. *Head Lice*—Lice, or tiny parasitic insects, are more likely to be a problem when the blood quality becomes more acidic. The overconsumption of meat and other animal proteins, simple sugars, tropical fruits, spices, and other more excessively yin items contributes to a more acidic blood quality. Lice will often disappear once these items are reduced and a centrally balanced diet is adopted. Common sense practices in regard to bathing, washing the hair, and overall cleanliness also help prevent infestation and complement a more balanced dietary approach.

8. *Insect Bites*—Children are more prone to mosquito bites, bee or wasp stings, and other insect bites when they overconsume sugar, concentrated sweeteners, tropical and other fruits, ice cream, and soft drinks. Children with more normally alkaline blood—which comes about from eating a more centrally balanced diet— tend to be bitten less frequently. Mosquitoes seem to know intuitively to avoid more yang quality blood, since it often coagulates before reaching the mosquito's stomach. This is fatal to the mosquito; hence they seem to prefer thinner, sweeter, and more yin blood.

The Macrobiotic Approach: The macrobiotic approach to skin problems is based on correcting the underlying dietary imbalances that lead to chronic imbalances in the blood and to skin discharges. A variety of natural home care applications can also help in relieving discomfort. However, instead of trying to interfere with the body's natural discharge of excess, it is far better to allow the excess to come out, while at the same time, removing the underlying cause.

Children with skin conditions can begin the standard macrobiotic diet with appropriate adjustments for their age and condition. It is, of course, important to reduce or avoid foods, such as those mentioned above, that contribute to each particular condition.

Within the standard macrobiotic diet, it is often helpful to reduce or limit the intake of animal foods, buckwheat products, raw fruits, concentrated sweeteners, flour products, nuts, nut butters, and oil, including vegetable oils. Again, these are general recommendations and need to be adapted to each circumstance. It is therefore helpful to contact an experienced macrobiotic advisor when implementing these or other dietary suggestions.

External applications that utilize natural products in the home can also be applied to relieve discomfort and to aid in improvement. These applications include:

1. *Rice Bran (Nuka) Skin Wash or Bath*—Nuka, or rice bran, can be purchased at most natural food stores. To prepare a skin wash, wrap nuka in cheesecloth. Place in warm water, squeeze, and shake. The nuka will dissolve and the water will turn yellowish and a white foam may form on the surface. Lightly wash the affected area several times with a towel or facecloth that has been dipped in the nuka water.

   Children with skin problems can also be given a bath in which nuka has been dissolved. Put about 3 to 5 tablespoons of nuka into a white cotton sock or a sack made of thin cotton cloth or cheesecloth. Tie the sack so that the nuka does not fall out. Place the sack in the bathwater and squeeze it until a milky liquid comes out. Mix the milky liquid in the water and use it to wash the skin, including the areas where the disorder is present. Rice bran contains natural oil that helps the skin return to a smooth and healthy condition. The hair can also be washed in nuka water.

   If you cannot find rice bran, rolled oats can be substituted. About 1/4 cup can be used. Nuka or oat applications may also be used to ease the itching and discomfort of poison ivy or insect bites.

2. *Dried Leaves and Sea Salt Skin Wash*—This application is helpful in extracting excess fat and oil and in helping the skin return to normal. Dry fresh daikon leaves (or purchase dried leaves at a natural food store) away from sunlight until they become brown and brittle. Boil 4 to 5 bunches of leaves with 4 to 5 quarts of water until the water turns brown. Add a medium-sized handful of sea salt and stir well. Dip a cotton cloth or towel into the liquid and squeeze it lightly. Apply it to the affected area, making repeated

applications until the skin becomes red. The hair can be washed frequently with this liquid in cases of head lice. This application may also be applied for insect bites or poison ivy.

3. *Daikon Juice*—The juice from freshly grated daikon is often helpful in relieving itching. Grate several tablespoons of fresh daikon. Dip sanitized cotton into the gratings, allowing the cotton to absorb the juice. Apply the juice directly to the area of the skin that is itching.

4. *Sesame Oil*—Sesame oil often helps soothe skin discomfort. It can be applied directly to the affected area. Either light or dark oil can be used.

5. *Tofu-Chlorophyll Plaster*—A tofu-chlorophyll plaster, described in the *Recipe and Home Care Guide*, can be applied when an insect bite or other skin disorder produces swelling. Apply directly to the affected area until the tofu becomes warm. Replace with a fresh application if necessary.

When children develop a skin condition, it is important to be careful in selecting natural vegetable fabrics for their clothing and sleeping materials. Cotton is preferable to wool or synthetics. Rice bran, oats, or natural vegetable soaps are preferable to chemical soaps or shampoos for regular use.

Skin disorders are often related to problems in two of the primary organs of discharge—the kidneys and intestines. The foods that underlie skin conditions are usually those that weaken these internal organs and diminish their capacity to discharge excess.

The intestines and kidneys respond to simple home applications along with proper eating. Warm towel compresses may be applied repeatedly to the middle back (kidneys) and abdomen (intestines) to strengthen these organs. These applications can be done for 5 to 10 minutes in each region, everyday or every other day while a child is recovering from a skin condition. Palm healing is also helpful in stimulating these organs. Apply the palms lightly to the middle back and then to the abdomen. Breathe as described in previous sections, and apply the hands for 10 to 15 minutes on each region.

Hyperactivity and Behavioral Problems

There is no rigid standard for human behavior. Every child is unique, with differences in constitution, diet, environment, and upbringing. These influences produce an endless variety in behavior and appearance. It is because of these differences that life is so interesting, joyful, and amusing.

Food and environment are primary in determining behavior. Both influence the child long before conception. They determine the quality of the parental reproductive cells and the genetic information they contain. They also determine the general pattern of the culture or society the child is born into, which in turn will influence how he or she will think and act. The child's constitution and condition are a product of diet and environment. Behavior is simply the expression of the child's constitution and daily condition.

Figure 15   The Origin of Behavior

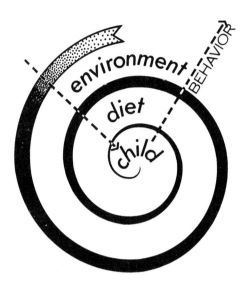

Today, many children have problems with learning, perception, and behavior. Many children have trouble learning basic reading, writing, spelling, and arithmetic. Some are consistently erratic in behavior. They cannot pay attention, are extreme in their emotions, and are unable to sit still. These children are often labeled as *hyperactive* or *hyperkinetic*. They may or may not have specific learning disabilities, although many children who are considered hyperactive are actually quite bright. Hyperactivity is actually a comprehensive term that usually includes these and other traits.

However, it is important to remember that children are normally active and energetic. They do not behave like adults, nor should they be expected to. It is necessary to be careful before labeling a child hyperactive, hyperkinetic, or learning disabled. All children learn at different rates. The important thing is not test scores, but whether children put forth their best efforts.

Behavior and learning problems are related to the modern, highly processed, artificial diet and to an increasingly unnatural lifestyle—including the use of synthetic materials in the home and at school. An extreme diet often interferes with the normal processes of learning and of normal or balanced behavior. An excessive intake of more yang items—such as meat, eggs, poultry, or refined salt—can produce emotional characteristics such as overly aggressive behavior, extreme stubbornness, or an overly self-centered attitude. These food items tend to narrow the child's scope of vision and reduce patience, endurance, and sociability. The body and mind become less flexible when more yang extremes are overconsumed.

The excessive intake of yin extremes also contributes to behavioral and learning disabilities. Refined sugar, artificial sweeteners, milk, ice cream, refined flour, chocolate, and additives and preservatives (more than 5,000 additives have been used in foods over the last twenty years) can cause more yin disintegrative symptoms such as inability to focus on visual images, sound, or thoughts, poor memory, a poor sense of balance, and lack of self-discipline.

In general, the symptoms of hyperactivity can be classified into two general categories, according to the primary foods that promote them. These include (1) symptoms influenced primarily by the overconsumption of more yang extremes; and (2) those which are influenced primarily by the overintake of more yin extremes. The most common symptoms of hyperactivity are classified below:

More Yin Symptoms:
- *Inability to focus* on one thing at a time, or to think concretely.
- *Confusion,* or inability to make order out of vibrations received by the brain.
- *No sense of direction or purpose.*
- *Mixing up common yin and yang distinctions* such as left and right, vertical and horizontal, inside and outside, front and back, or beginning and ending.
- *Being out of touch with the body,* including not being aware of certain parts of the body, a lack of coordination, or loss of control over bodily functions.
- *Continual movement,* especially involving small, nervous movements of the hands, fingers, or other parts of the body, including minor twitching or shaking.
- *Slow development,* for example, learning to walk, talk, or read later than normal.

More Yang Symptoms:
- *Rigidity in body and mind,* including extreme stubbornness or literal-mindedness.
- *Continual movement,* especially involving the large muscles of the body, for example, continually getting up from a chair, always running rather than walking, jumping up and down, or rocking back and forth.
- *Overly rapid development,* for example, walking, crawling, or talking earlier than normal; or skipping stages of development.
- *Impatience or lack of inhibition.*
- *Overly rough or destructive behavior,* including violent outbursts of temper.
- *Aggressiveness toward others,* including bullying, harassing, or fighting with other children, or cruelty toward pets or others in a defenseless position.
- *Extreme ego-centeredness,* to the point of being unaware or insensitive to others.

The diet of most hyperactive children is generally extreme at both ends—for example, meat, eggs, and poultry on one hand; and plenty of sugar, tropical fruit, chemicals, and refined and processed foods on the other. Their actions and behavior therefore tend to swing unpredictably back and forth between both extremes. Underlying both extremes is often the excessive overconsumption of milk and other dairy products.

When children have a tendency toward hyperactivity, artificial substances in the immediate environment often trigger symptoms. They frequently react to products ranging from chemicalized toothpaste to felt-tipped markers. A list of substances that can trigger extreme reactions in hyperactive children is presented in Table 8:

As mentioned previously, we recommend using more natural materials in the home. Clothing, home fixtures, toys, soap, shampoo, toothpaste, laundry detergents, and kitchen utensils made from natural materials are preferred over those made from synthetic substances. Natural materials are less likely to trigger a reaction.

Current Approaches: Current approaches to hyperactivity include nutritional management, behavior modification, counseling, special education programs, and drug therapy. The management of hyperactivity through diet includes a variety of approaches, most notably that developed by the late Dr. Ben Feingold. Dr. Feingold reported success in reducing hyperactivity in about 50 percent of the cases under his care. The *Feingold Diet* involves primarily reducing or eliminating the intake of more extremely yin items, including preservatives such as BHT and BHA, refined sugar, and chemical additives, including artificial flavors and colors. Things such as aspirin, bell peppers, chili powder, coffee, oranges, spearmint and pepper-mint, commercial tea, and tomatoes, all of which contain *salicylates*—acidic compounds found in fruits and other more yin foods—have also been associated with hyperactive reactions and are often eliminated from the diet.

The avoidance of more yin foods and other substances would lessen the more yin symptoms of hyperactivity. However, at least 50 percent of hyperactive children do not respond to this approach, an indication that many cases of hyperactivity result from the overconsumption of more extremely yang foods or from the combined effect of both extremes. A dietary approach that takes both aspects into consideration is therefore necessary.

The other common approach to hyperactivity involves giving children amphetamine drugs such as *Dexedrine* and *Ritalin*. Like coffee, these drugs are often used as mental stimulants, and when taken regularly, they weaken the motion centers of the brain, and cause the child to become less hyperactive. They tend to activate the front portions of the brain, artificially stimulating the ability to focus thinking.

For the most part, drugs are an unsatisfactory response to behavioral problems. They are purely symptomatic, and do not address nor change the underlying causes of the problem. There have been no long-term studies of the side effects of the psychoactive drugs given for hyperactivity. In the macrobiotic view, these drugs are classified as extremely yin. Being extreme, they weaken the nervous system and internal organs. The long-term effects of chronic drug use include:

(1)   Dulling of the body's automatic functions—Drugs such as amphetamines initially activate the autonomic nervous system and its two complementary branches: the *orthosympathetic* and *parasympathetic* systems. However, chronic

**Table 8   Examples of Environmental Irritants that Can Trigger
an Increase in the Hyperactivity of an Exposed Child**

Clothing
any polyester fabric or item
polyester bedding
permanent-press clothes not yet washed
TRIS flame retardant in clothes

House fixtures
blown-in insulation with
    urea-formaldehyde
smell from new carpeting
fluorescent lighting
oil, natural gas and coal heating systems
propane appliances
vinyl wallpaper
interior of new mobile homes
glue used in flooring, wallpaper,
    and paneling

Playthings
ball-point ink on skin
invisible ink on skin
felt-tip marker on skin
colored chalk
chalk dust in the air
finger paint
scratch and sniff books
putty-like, slimy, and clay-like
    modeling compounds
caps and fireworks
white powder inside balloons
Easter-egg dye

Toiletries
alcohol on skin
hand lotion
colored and perfumed soap
facial powder
eye shadow
fingernail polish
lipsticks to prevent chapping
perfume
after-shave lotion
hair spray
toothpaste
bubble bath
dental cleaning agents
fluoride treatment

adhesive bandages
colored and flavored medicine

Cleaning and polishing agents
disinfectant containing methyl
    salicylate
pine fragrance soap
furniture and floor wax
oven cleaner
pine fragrance liquid cleaner
rug shampoo
colored dishwasher detergent
fabric softener sheets for dryer

Paper products
colored or scented paper towels
colored or scented facial tissue
colored or scented bathroom
    tissue
colored cupcake liners
paper wiping rags

Workshop chemicals
fumes of paint, varnish, etc.
glue (including postage stamps and
    envelope seals)
gasoline fumes
gasoline or oil leak
chlorine in swimming pool
airborne particles of paint or varnish
    from sanding finished wood
freshly poured blacktop

Aromatics
mothballs
incense
scented candle
air freshener
dog and cat repellent
aerosol spray cans
smoke from a fire
smoke from a menthol cigarette

Plastics
old teflon pans, flaking
polyurethane food-storage bowls
plastic food wrap
waterbeds

Reprinted from *The Hyperactive Child and the Family* by John F. Taylor, Dodd, Mead &
Company, 1980, pp. 54–55, with permission.

usage weakens the parasympathetic system and results in a loss of quickness and accuracy in adapting to the environment. Many parents have reported that medicated children frequently act drugged or over-medicated. Impairment of motor functions makes a child more accident prone.

(2)   Decreased sensitivity—The continual use of drugs causes the cells of the nervous system to become semipermanently expanded, thus diminishing their reactive powers and leading to decreased sensitivity.

(3)   A loss of clarity—The intake of extremely yin stimulant drugs weakens the inner area of the brain, especially the midbrain, while activating the more yin surrounding cortex. The more yang motion centers of the brain are also weakened. The midbrain represents the focal point for gathering information from the entire nervous system in the form of stimuli. It simultaneously relays information outward to appropriate parts of the body in the form of various responses such as speech and decisions to act. In hyperactivity, "gatekeepers" which control input to the midbrain do not function properly. Information comes in without being properly ordered. The relay of information from the midbrain to the various parts of the body is also disrupted. Instead of a more orderly or controlled relay of information, the brain of the hyperactive child sends a variety of poorly coordinated, uncontrolled, and contradictory signals to the various parts of the body.

In order for this key function to operate well, the innermost orbit of the nervous system, which is situated at the midbrain, must be tightly coiled and highly energized, with its cells compact. The habitual expansion produced by drugs has a damaging effect on mental clarity after a period of time, although the initial impression may be one of relaxation and heightened clarity.

(4)   Weakening of internal organs—Certain of our internal organs rely primarily on contraction for their normal activity, and others depend more on relaxation, although both tendencies exist in each organ. Like the midbrain and the motion centers of the brain, the major relatively more yang organs tend to be weakened by habitual use of drugs. They include the spleen, pancreas, heart, lungs, liver, and kidneys. Which of these are affected to a noticeable extent depends on a number of individual considerations, including constitution, previous illnesses, former diet, and so on.

(5)   Decline of reproductive ability—Giving children drugs during childhood could impair their future reproductive abilities. The reproductive organs—the ovaries and testes—are more yang and compact. They are easily debilitated by the intake of extremely yin substances. Infertility and reproductive disorders are approaching epidemic proportions in modern society. Many of these problems can be traced to the use of drugs or medications during childhood or adolescence. Continual drug use creates imbalances in the quantity and quality of hormone secretion, such as *testosterone*, due to abnormal stimulation of adrenal, gonadal, and pituitary glands. This imbalance in the hormone system, when combined with

general weakening of the nervous system, leads to debility and irregular functioning of the reproductive system. The debilitating effects of drugs are particularly acute during puberty and adolescence when the hormonal functions connected with sexual maturation become operative.

(6)   Degeneration of blood quality and weakening of natural immunity—Drugs such as those given for hyperactivity tend to destroy the intestinal flora which are essential for smooth absorption of food into the bloodstream. The liver, spleen, and bone marrow, involved in the continued regeneration of red blood cells, are adversely affected by prolonged drug use. Therefore, children who already suffer from illnesses associated with lowered blood quality—such as leukemia, anemia, diabetes, asthma, allergies, and skin disorders—could experience a worsening of their condition after prolonged drug use.

Drugs also weaken the body's autoimmune system. Functions such as the ability of the liver to detoxify poisons and the ability of specialized cells in the lymphatic and bloodstreams to identify and ingest foreign substances are especially weakened. The cooperative functioning of *T cells* and *B cells* as part of the body's immune response is disrupted by the intake of drugs. Drug use is a contributive factor in many cases of AIDS and other immune deficiency disorders.

(7)   Psychological and social impairment—These various manifestations of lessened physical and mental vitality combine to impede the individual and social development of the children burdened with them. Children who are given drugs for hyperactivity could very easily develop psychological dependence on drugs and on artificial or superficial methods of dealing with problems.

Aside from these possible long-term consequences, there are many documented short-term side effects associated with the drugs given for hyperactivity.

For example, *Ritalin*, a drug recommended for a variety of emotional problems, has the potential to produce such immediate side effects as skin rash, fever, scaling or itching of the skin, blood clotting disorders, nausea, dizziness, irregular heartbeat, drowsiness, headache, loss of appetite, stunting of growth, and others.

An approach that carries the risk of potentially damaging side effects—both short- and long-term—while ignoring the underlying cause of hyperactivity is obviously unsatisfactory. Many parents are justifiably distrustful of the use of behavior modifying drugs to control hyperactivity. Most people tend to favor nutritional approaches to behavioral problems.

The Macrobiotic Approach: A more holistic approach to hyperactivity involves changing the underlying causes. As a first step, parents need to reflect on their way of eating and on the way of eating of the family as a whole, together with their overall manner of living and relating to each other. Hyperactivity is the product of the lifestyle of the family as a whole, including daily dietary practice. Approaches that isolate the hyperactive child without considering other members of the family are at best partial and cannot be thought of as solutions.

As a first step toward overcoming hyperactivity, therefore, we recommend that all members of the child's family change their way of eating toward the standard macrobiotic diet described in Chapter One. Appropriate modifications are of course required for each person. The daily life recommendations presented in Chapter One can also be applied, especially the substitution of more natural products for more artificial ones in the home.

In cases where children have not been placed on medication, the transition to a macrobiotic diet can proceed in a more smooth and straightforward manner. As parents learn how to cook and the family as a whole changes its diet, the hyperactive child can begin to eat according to general macrobiotic guidelines appropriate for age, condition, and activity.

Children who have been placed on medication need a more gradual period of moderate transition. An overly rapid or inflexible approach to adopting macrobiotics is not recommended. The following general guidelines may be applied in these circumstances.

1. Whole grains may account for 40 to 60 percent of food intake. Grains may include both whole grains and flour products such as high quality traditional sourdough breads, noodles, *seitan* (a wheat gluten product often used as a meat substitute), fu, and others, and may be prepared in a variety of styles—pressure-cooked, boiled, served in soups, casseroles, breads, pancakes, noodles, porridge, muffins, crackers, and so on.
2. Soups may be included daily. Light miso or tamari broth soups may be served once a day. Whole grain, vegetable, and bean soups may also be included if desired.
3. Vegetables may account for 20 to 30 percent of daily intake, and may be prepared in a variety of styles. In addition to cooked vegetables, a small portion of raw salad and pickles may be included regularly if desired.
4. Beans may account for about 10 percent of daily intake, cooked in a variety of styles. Traditionally processed soy products such as tempeh, tofu, dried tofu, and natto may be eaten daily in addition to beans.
5. Cooked sea vegetables may account for about 5 percent of daily intake. Because of their high mineral content they are particularly useful in restoring those parts of the nervous system damaged by drugs and other more extremely yin items.
6. Fish and seafood, nuts and seeds, snacks, and seasonal fruits may account for roughly another 5 percent of daily intake, varying with individual desire and needs and the time of year—e.g., more fruit in summer than in winter, and fish on a more regular basis during the autumn and winter.
7. Liquids may be consumed as freely as desired, although sugared or artificial soft drinks, milk, and tropical or semitropical fruit juices are best avoided.
8. Guidelines for seasonings, use of condiments, cooking styles, variety of foods, etc., generally follow those presented in Chapters One and Three.

These general suggestions, if followed in a common sense manner with appropriate adjustments and guidance from an experienced macrobiotic adviser, can lead to a gradual restoration of more normal behavior. Macrobiotic dietary and way of life suggestions may be combined with other approaches such as behavior modification, family counseling, and remedial teaching programs for academic deficiency. The effectiveness of these approaches will be greatly enhanced when combined with the practice of macrobiotics.

As the new dietary pattern becomes more well established, parents will notice gradual improvement of behavior. The child will become able to sit still, to concentrate, to be more steady in thought and emotion. The child will gradually become more self-controlled, and more responsive to parents, teachers, and others.

In many cases, the condition may improve to the point where it is possible to reduce or discontinue the use of medication, without any worsening of behavioral symptoms or decline in learning abilities. The question of when or how gradually to discontinue medication is a highly individual issue and is best approached with care and in consultation with the appropriate medical professional. As a general rule, reliance on drugs or medications is best withdrawn slowly rather than all at once, in stages that follow the gradual improvement of condition and that permit a regular reassessment of dosages and their effects. Depending on how successful the family is in adopting the macrobiotic guidelines, the drugs that are commonly given for hyperactivity can be gradually withdrawn over several months. Again, this is a matter that should be discussed with a health-care professional.

It is important to remember that once drugs are discontinued, their effects do not disappear overnight, even though the overall condition is steadily improving. Hyperactive children are often given drugs daily for extended periods. The amount of time needed to recover from the effects of these medications are generally as follows:

Table 9

Duration of daily medication	Period to recover from the effects
1–4 weeks	4 months
1–3 months	1 year
4–6 months	2 years
6 months–1 year	3 years
1–2 years	4–5 years
3–5 years	6–7 years

Until the period of recovery is complete, it is recommended that the complete range of foods recommended as a part of macrobiotic practice be included on a regular basis. The percentage of grains is best kept within the general 40 to 60 percent range while other foods may be increased according to need and personal desire. For example, sea vegetables may be 10 percent instead of 5 percent, or beans and bean products may be 15 percent instead of 10 percent. If the child experiences problems with the withdrawal of drugs, the percentage of vegetables, fruits, and/or fish may be increased and the percentage of grains decreased slightly until the symptoms improve.

During the period of recovery from the previous use of drugs, improvement is gradual but may be interrupted by occasional recurrence of symptoms associated with the effects of drugs. These minor relapses may include occasional strange or disturbing dreams during sleep, overexcitement or depression; hypersensitivity; general anxiety or feelings of fear; laziness or sloppiness; irregularity in writing, speaking, or difficulty with schoolwork; frequent changes of mind and difficulty in making decisions or thinking clearly; low resistance to cold weather or infection; slow rate of injury healing; periodic drowsiness or loss of appetite; difficulty going to sleep or sleeping soundly; and others.

Which of these symptoms will appear depends on the former medical history of each child, but none is necessarily cause for serious concern, since they generally disappear of themselves as the healing process proceeds. However, until the period of recovery is complete, children who were placed on drugs may experience any of these symptoms.

When children experience behavioral problems, and while they are recovering a more natural balance, parents need to devote time and energy into creating a loving, patient, and supportive atmosphere at home. Parents can also meet with teachers and others with whom the child has regular contact, such as a minister, or rabbi, or the parents of classmates or friends. Explain your situation to them whenever necessary, including the child's dietary practice, and ask for their support and encouragement.

The macrobiotic approach, when combined with a loving, warm, and under-standing attitude on the part of parents, teachers, and other members of the family, offers a sane and humane approach to hyperactivity and other behavioral disorders. It offers children with these problems an opportunity to become healthy and productive members of society and to realize their fullest potential, free from artificial dependence.

Accidents, Emergencies, and First Aid

Accidents are a major source of injury and suffering for children today. Like physical and mental disorders, they often have their root in daily diet and way of life. Alcohol abuse, for example, is a leading cause of automobile accidents, including those among young people.

As a fundamental way of preventing accidents, parents can provide children with a naturally balanced diet and an orderly, yet flexible, way of life. Being con-tinually aware of their day to day condition and eating is also important in accident prevention.

Parents naturally possess an intuitive sense in regard to their children's health and well-being. A mother will often know instinctively whether her children are safe or in danger, or whether they are healthy or sick, even when apart from them.

Parents' intuitive awareness of their children's condition is strengthened by a balanced natural diet. Many animals have an instinctive awareness of danger and are thus able to avoid it. Animals live with the rhythms of nature and eat natural unprocessed food.

The modern highly processed diet dulls the capacity for natural intuition. Items such as sugar, alcohol, and drugs and medications weaken the nervous system. When this happens, our ability to avoid potential hazards or to respond quickly and appropriately should an emergency arise, becomes diminished. Foods such as meat, cheese, milk, and other fatty items also dull the nervous system. Excess in the organs, tissues, and glands diminishes our receptivity to the environment and makes it more difficult to respond appropriately. Many people today have a layer of hard fat just below the skin. (This condition is common in thin people as well as in the overweight.) Not only does this condition interfere with the body's ability to discharge toxic excess, but it also reduces sensitivity to the social and physical environment. A person with this condition is often insensitive to potential hazards and may become overly confident or careless.

We recommend that all parents eat well and encourage their children to eat well in order to avoid accidents. Parents also need to learn the basics of first aid in case an emergency does arise. Parents can familiarize themselves with basic fundamentals such as:

1. How to deal with wounds, including first aid for severe bleeding and methods to prevent infection.
2. How to deal with specific injuries, including those involving the head, eyes, back, chest, and so on.
3. How to recognize and treat shock.
4. How to deal with breathing emergencies, including artificial respiration. Water and boating safety are also important.
5. How to deal with choking and swallowed objects.
6. What to do in the case of accidental poisoning.
7. How to classify and treat burns.
8. How to deal with frostbite and exposure to cold.
9. What to do in the case of heat stroke, heat exhaustion, and heat cramps.
10. How to respond to sudden illness such as fainting, convulsion, or febrile seizures.
11. How to prepare dressings and bandages, and how to make an appropriate first aid kit.
12. How to respond to bone and joint injuries, including sprains, fractures, and dislocations.
13. What to do for foreign objects in the ears, eyes, and nose.
14. How to respond in an emergency, for example, how to administer appropriate first aid, enlist help from bystanders, contact the appropriate emergency medical services (EMS) personnel, and be of help to the medical staff at the hospital emergency room.
15. How to adjust the child's daily diet during recovery from accident or injury.

There are many good books that deal with the basics of first aid and emergency care. We recommend that all parents consult texts such as *Standard First Aid and*

Personal Safety published by the American Red Cross. The macrobiotic approach to first aid and emergency care is outlined in our recently published book, *Macrobiotic Home Remedies* (see the Bibliography). Please refer to this text for more specific guidance and advice. Once an emergency situation has been stabilized with the appropriate medical assistance, we recommend contacting a qualified macrobiotic advisor or educational center for additional suggestions and guidance.

Conclusion: Toward a Planetary Family

The future exists today. Long after we leave this planet, our children and descendants will continue. Providing them with the basis for a healthy and productive life is our most important priority as parents.

Creating a healthy family is the work of God. The family is a replica of the universe and the creative process that gives life to everything.

We all cherish the memory of a happy family life. The warmth and love that exist between mother and father, between parents and children, and between brothers and sisters can be found nowhere else. Macrobiotic living makes this type of family life possible for everyone, now and in the future. It is a way of life that is essential for everyone who wishes to create a wonderful happy family and beautiful, intelligent, and healthy children.

Today, our world is in danger. Degenerative diseases, nuclear war, and mental illness could destroy the human spirit and undercut the future of life on this planet. Strong and healthy families, and bright, happy children are needed now more than ever. Children who receive the benefit of a macrobiotic upbringing are qualified to guide and inspire humanity toward a bright and positive future.

Macrobiotic child care is a direct method for the eventual realization of planetary health and peace. Those who share a similiar quality of food are like members of an extended family, no matter where they live. Beginning with ourselves and our immediate families, let us invite all people to become members of the planetary family of the earth.

In the future, our sense of family unity can be extended to include everyone on the planet. Our spiritual connections can also extend to our ancestors for thousands of generations. Our sense of home and belonging can extend to the entire surface of the planet and beyond. Humanity can share love, understanding, and trust with one another and can be free to realize its most cherished dreams.

The way to achieve this is simple. It is based on love for nature, the universe, for other people and all beings. Let us hope that in the future, all families embrace it and use it to realize love and peace on our beautiful planet.

Chapter **5**

Recipe and Home Care Guide

In this chapter, we present instructions for making special dishes and preparations for children. Included are dishes, teas, and external applications referred to in the previous chapter. These recipes and home applications are recommended for use as part of a child's daily diet and home care during the natural recovery from illness or discomfort, and not as a substitute for appropriate medical attention when necessary.

We have also included a section with special dishes and foods for more general use, adapted from Aveline's seminars in Boston.

Variety is important when cooking for children. We recommend a wide selection of foods and cooking methods. The recipes presented here are only a small sample of the thousands of possibilities in macrobiotic cooking. More complete guidelines for family cooking are presented in *Aveline Kushi's Complete Guide to Macrobiotic Cooking, Introducing Macrobiotic Cooking,* and other cookbooks listed in the Bibliography.

Step by step guidelines for preparing complete meals for children are presented in the companion volume to this book, *Macrobiotic Family Favorites: Cooking for Healthy Children.* Please consult *Family Favorites* for ideas when planning meals for children.

In the following recipes, it is advisable that, whenever possible, the ingredients—grains, beans, vegetables, etc.—be organic, and that the processed items—miso, tamari soy sauce, tofu, etc.—be of the highest quality. In addition, it is recommended that spring or well water be used in the preparation of foods and beverages.

Style Note for Recipes
---

oz — ounce	tsp — teaspoon
lb — pound	350°F. — 350 degrees Fahrenheit
Tbsp — tablespoon	5% — 5 percent

Special Dishes for Children

Special Rice Cream

> 1 cup brown rice (short grain)
> 5 cups water
> 1 strip kombu, 1 inch long, soaked 3–4 minutes

Wash the rice very well in cold water. Put the kombu in a pressure cooker. Place the rice in a skillet and dry-roast until golden brown, constantly moving the grain from side to side to evenly roast and prevent burning. Place the roasted rice in the pressure cooker and add water. Cover the cooker and bring to pressure. When the pressure is up, place a flame deflector under the pot and cook for approximately 1-1/2 hours. Remove from flame and allow the pressure to come down naturally before opening.

Make a sack out of sterile cotton cheesecloth and place the cooked rice and rice liquid inside. Squeeze out all of the creamy liquid. The rice pulp remaining in the sack can be set aside and used in making bread.

Place the special rice cream in a saucepan. Add a little sweetener such as barley malt or rice honey to the rice cream if desired (about 1 teaspoon sweetener per cup of rice cream). Heat the rice cream and serve. To store, place the rice cream in a tightly sealed glass bottle or jar and keep in a cool place or in the refrigerator. Reheat before serving.

If the baby is very young (two to six months), use 10 cups of water instead of 5 to make the rice cream moister and easier for the baby to swallow.

Soft Grain Cereals (Rice, millet, barley, etc.)

> 1 cup grain
> 5 cups water
> 1 strip kombu, 1 inch long, soaked 3–4 minutes

Wash the grain and place in a bowl. Add water and soak 6–8 hours or overnight. Place the kombu, soaked grain and grain soaking water in a pressure cooker. Cover the cooker and bring to pressure. When the pressure is up, place a flame deflector under the pot. Reduce the flame to medium-low and cook approximately 1 hour. Remove from flame and allow the pressure to come down naturally before opening.

For babies, place the grain in a suribachi and grind to a smooth consistency. For children over one year old, either grind slightly or serve as is. If desired, sweeten this dish occasionally with a little barley malt or rice honey.

Root vegetables, squash, round vegetables, and so on, can be cooked with the grain from time to time to make variety for the baby.

Arepa

> 1 cup dried corn
> 1 cup wood ash
> 2 cups water
> 1 strip kombu, 1 inch long, soaked 3–4 minutes

Place washed corn in a bowl, cover with water, and soak overnight. Remove corn and drain. Place corn, kombu, wood ash and water in a pressure cooker, and bring to pressure. Reduce the flame to low and place a flame deflector under the pot. Cook for about 80 to 90 minutes, until the corn is soft. Remove from flame and allow the pressure to come down naturally before opening.

Place the corn in a strainer or colander, and wash it very well to remove all wood ash. In a grinder, mash the cooked corn to a thick paste or dough. After grinding, it may be necessary to add a little water to make a thick dough. Form small amounts of the dough into cakes or patties about 1/2 inch thick and 3 inches in diameter. Place the cakes in a dry, heated skillet and fry or toast until golden brown on each side. If a hard skin on the outside is not desired, steam the arepa instead of pan-frying them. Steamed arepa become very soft and are especially good for children.

Dried Daikon

> $\frac{1}{2}$ cup dried daikon, soaked 5–7 minutes
> 1 strip kombu, 4–5 inches long, soaked 5 minutes
> $\frac{1}{4}$ cup celery, sliced on a thick diagonal
> $\frac{1}{4}$ cup squash (such as buttercup), cut in 1-inch chunks
> $\frac{1}{4}$ cup carrots, cut in 1-inch chunks
> water

pinch of sea salt (optional depending on age)
tamari (optional depending on age)

After soaking the kombu, slice it into 1-inch squares and place it in the pot. Slice the soaked daikon into 1-inch lengths and place on top of the kombu. Next, layer the celery, squash, and carrots in that order on top of the daikon. Place about 1/2 inch of water in the pot and add a very small pinch of sea salt. Cover and bring to a boil. Reduce the flame to low and simmer for approximately 35–40 minutes, or until very soft. For a child over two years old, season with a small amount of tamari at this point. Continue to cook until almost all of the liquid is gone. Mix and place in a serving dish.

It is better not to give dried daikon to very young children, as its harder texture may make it a little difficult to digest. Instead, give them the sweet juice left over from cooking it. After the child is about two years old, we can begin serving it, but be sure to cook until the daikon is very soft. Dried daikon may also sometimes be cooked with vegetables, in soups or in grain dishes.

Dried Tofu

Young children may find it a little difficult to digest dried tofu unless it is properly cooked. Also, unless cooked together with vegetables and a little tamari, dried tofu is somewhat tasteless. Not having a particular taste of its own, it absorbs the flavors of whatever else it is cooked with.

To properly prepare dried tofu for children, soak it several minutes in warm water, rinse it under cold water and then pressure-cook it together with whatever vegetables are desired. For children over two years old, season with a little tamari.

3 slices dried tofu, soaked, rinsed and cut into 1-inch cubes
1 strip kombu, 3–4 inches long, soaked and sliced into 1-inch squares
$\frac{1}{4}$ cup onions, sliced in thick half-moons
$\frac{1}{4}$ cup carrots, sliced in 1-inch chunks
$\frac{1}{2}$ cup cabbage, sliced in thick chunks
water
tamari

Place the kombu in a pressure cooker. Add the onions, carrots and cabbage. Place the dried tofu in the cooker. Add about 1/4 inch of water, a small amount of tamari and cover. Place cooker on a medium flame and bring to pressure. Reduce the flame to low and cook approximately 10 minutes. Remove from flame and allow the pressure to come down.

Dried Seitan (Fu)

Dried seitan, or fu as it is called, is an easily digested food which children can eat quite often. It is a flour product, but because it is moist and does not make children tight or contracted, it is recommended highly for children. Fu should be soaked first and then cooked very soft with vegetables or in soups. There are many varieties of fu to choose from.

> **1 cup fu, soaked and sliced**
> **1 strip kombu, 3–4 inches long, soaked and thinly sliced**
> **$\frac{1}{2}$ cup onions, sliced in thick half-moons**
> **$\frac{1}{4}$ cup carrots, sliced on a thin diagonal**
> **water**
> **1 cup broccoli flowerettes**
> **$\frac{1}{2}$ cup fresh tofu, cubed**
> **tamari (optional depending on age)**

Place the kombu in a heavy pot. Add the onions, carrots and fu. Add approximately 2 cups of water. Cover and bring to a boil. Reduce the flame to low and simmer until vegetables are tender (5–7 minutes). Add the broccoli and tofu, and simmer another 5 minutes or so, until soft. Season with a small amount of tamari and continue to simmer about 5 minutes longer. Mix and remove.

Noodles

Children can eat noodles often for meals or snacks as they are moist and easily digested. The best types for children are whole wheat spaghetti, elbows, shells, whole wheat udon or whole wheat somen. Soba can be used very occasionally for older children but usually is not recommended for babies under one year old.

> **4 oz package somen**
> **3 cups water**
> **1 strip kombu, 3–4 inches long, soaked 3–4 minutes**
> **1 shiitake mushroom, soaked**
> **tamari (optional depending on age)**
> **$\frac{1}{2}$ cup Chinese cabbage, sliced on a thick diagonal**
> **$\frac{1}{2}$ sheet nori, toasted and cut into 1-inch squares**

Cook the somen as you would any noodle (they cook very quickly), rinse under cold water and drain. In another pot add the 3 cups of water for broth. Add the kombu and shiitake, cover and bring to a boil. Reduce the flame to low and simmer about 10 minutes. Remove the kombu and shiitake and set aside for future use. Season the broth with a small amount of tamari, and simmer several minutes longer.

Place the Chinese cabbage in a pot with about $\frac{1}{4}$ inch of boiling water, cover and simmer about 4–5 minutes, until tender.

Place the noodles in a bowl. Pour broth over the noodles. Garnish with Chinese cabbage and several squares of nori and serve.

Mochi

> 1 cup sweet rice, washed and soaked 6–8 hours
> 1¼ cups water
> pinch of sea salt for older children

Place the rice, water and sea salt in a pressure cooker and cook as you would regular rice. When done, remove cover after the pressure comes down and place the rice in a heavy wooden bowl. Pound the rice with a mochi pounder, heavy pestle or wooden mallet until all the grains are crushed and sticky. The texture should be quite smooth. Good mochi takes at least 30–45 minutes of pounding.

Form the mochi into squares, cakes or rectangles about ½ inch thick and place them on a lightly floured baking sheet. Allow the mochi to dry, uncovered, for 1–2 days. After this drying period you may store in the refrigerator until using.

To cook the mochi, you may toast it in a dry skillet until each side is golden brown and has puffed up.

Mochi may be steamed, baked, sautéed in a little oil for older children, added to soups and stews, deep-fried, broiled or roasted in a dry skillet as above. To eat, serve plain, with a strip of toasted nori wrapped around it, or dipped in a little warm barley malt or rice honey. For older children, mochi can also be topped with a couple of drops of tamari.

Azuki-Chestnut-Raisins

> ½ cup azuki beans, soaked 6–8 hours
> 1 strip kombu, 3–4 inches long, soaked and sliced in 1-inch cubes
> ½ cup dried chestnuts, soaked 6–8 hours
> ¼ cup raisins
> 2½–3 cups water
> pinch of sea salt (optional depending on age)

Place the kombu in a heavy pot. Add the azuki beans, chestnuts, and raisins. Add the water (which can include the soaking water from the azuki beans and chestnuts). Bring to a boil, cover and reduce the flame to low. Simmer for about 2 hours. At this point, add the sea salt if cooking for an older child and continue to simmer another 30 minutes. Additional cold water may be added from time to time if necessary to keep the beans from burning or becoming too dry.

Occasionally, if necessary, the beans, chestnuts and raisins may be pressure-cooked for about 50 minutes. In this case season when done.

Rice and Lotus Seeds

> 1 cup brown rice
> ½ cup lotus seeds, soaked 3–4 hours
> 1½ cups water
> pinch of sea salt

Put rice, lotus seeds and water in a pressure cooker. Place the pressure cooker, uncovered, on a low flame and cook for about 10–15 minutes. Add the sea salt and cover. Raise flame to medium-high, and bring to pressure. Place a flame deflector under the cooker and reduce flame to medium-low. Cook for 50 minutes. Remove from flame and allow pressure to come down. Remove cover and place the rice in a wooden bowl.

Keeping Children Healthy

Simple Fever ────────────────────────────────

▪ *Special dishes and preparations:*

Dried Daikon Tea

> **1 Tbsp dried daikon**
> **2 cups water**

Place the dried daikon and water in a saucepan. Bring to a boil. Cover and reduce the flame to medium-low. Simmer until only 1 cup of liquid remains. Strain the liquid to remove the daikon. Small children may be given ½ cup.

Shiitake Tea

> **1 shiitake mushroom**
> **2 cups water**

Place the shiitake and water in a saucepan. Bring to a boil. Cover and reduce the flame to medium-low. Simmer until only 1 cup of liquid remains. Remove the shiitake and give approximately ½ cup to small children. For babies only about 1 teaspoon is enough. Older children may have 1 cup.

Dried Daikon and Shiitake Tea

> **1 Tbsp dried daikon**
> **1 shiitake mushroom**
> **2 cups water**

Place daikon, shiitake and water in a saucepan. Bring to a boil. Cover and reduce the flame to medium-low. Simmer until only 1 cup of liquid remains, then strain to remove the shiitake and daikon. For babies give only 1 teaspoon, for small children ½ cup, for older children 1 cup.

Grated Daikon Tea *(For older children)*

> 1 Tbsp fresh grated daikon
> pinch of fresh grated ginger ($\frac{1}{8}$ tsp)
> 1–2 drops tamari
> bancha tea

Place the daikon, ginger and tamari in a tea cup. Pour hot bancha tea over it. Mix and drink hot or warm.

Grated Sour Apple

> 1 sour green apple (Granny Smith)
> 2 grains sea salt (omit for babies)

Grate half of the sour green apple, including skin, and place it in a piece of sterile cheesecloth. Squeeze out all of the juice. Place the juice in a saucepan and heat. For small children (not for babies) add a couple grains of sea salt from the beginning. Drink warm or hot.

Grate the remaining $\frac{1}{2}$ apple and make applesauce with it.

For small babies give only 1 teaspoon. Older children may receive $\frac{1}{2}$–1 cup depending on their age.

Cereal Grain Tea

> $\frac{1}{4}$ cup brown rice
> 1 quart water

Wash the rice and dry-roast it over a medium flame, until golden brown, stirring constantly to prevent burning. Place the water in a teapot or saucepan. Add the roasted rice, and bring to a boil. Reduce the flame to low and simmer about 10–15 minutes.

■ *Home care:*

Green Vegetable Plaster

> 1 bunch leafy greens (such as collard, kale, watercress)

Chop washed greens very fine and place in a suribachi. Grind the greens well. If they are very watery, mix in a little pastry flour to hold the mixture together. Place the mashed greens on a piece of cotton cheesecloth or cotton linen to form a layer about $\frac{1}{2}$ inch thick. Apply directly to the forehead or other part of the body. Change every 2–3 hours.

Tofu-Green Vegetable Plaster

$\frac{1}{2}$ lb fresh tofu
several leafy greens (such as collard, kale, watercress)
5% fresh grated ginger
pastry flour (optional)

Chop the greens very fine and grind well in a suribachi. Place the tofu and ginger in the suribachi and grind to a thick paste. Place the paste on a clean piece of cotton cheesecloth or cotton linen creating a layer about $\frac{1}{2}$ inch thick. Apply directly to the forehead or other part of the body. Change every 2–3 hours.

Tofu Plaster

$\frac{1}{2}$ lb tofu, drained
10–20% pastry flour
5% fresh grated ginger

Place the tofu in a suribachi and grind. Add the pastry flour and grated ginger. Mix well. Place the tofu mixture about $\frac{1}{2}$ inch thick on a clean piece of cotton cheesecloth or cotton linen. Apply directly to the forehead or other part of the body. Change every 2–3 hours.

Stomachache ——————————————————————

■ *Special dishes and preparations:*

Ume-Sho-Kuzu

For very small children

$\frac{1}{2}$ tsp kuzu
1 cup water
1 very small piece umeboshi (about half the size of the nail on your little finger)

Dilute the kuzu in about 1 teaspoon water until dissolved. Add remaining water and the umeboshi. Place on a high flame, stirring constantly to prevent lumping. When the mixture begins to boil, reduce the flame to low and simmer about 1 minute. Drink hot or warm.

For older children

1 tsp kuzu
1 cup water

¼–½ umeboshi plum depending on child's age
1–2 drops of tamari

Prepare same as above. Add the tamari at the end of cooking, when the flame is reduced to low, and simmer for 1 minute.

Ume-Sho Bancha

1 cup hot bancha
¼–½ umeboshi plum
1–2 drops tamari

Place umeboshi plum and tamari in a teacup. Pour the hot bancha over it and stir. Drink hot or warm.

Ume-Bancha Tea

1 cup hot bancha
¼–½ umeboshi plum

Prepare same as above.

Baked Umeboshi Plums or Pits

Place a whole umeboshi plum in a cast iron skillet and cover. Preheat the oven to 300°F. and bake until completely black and brittle. Place the baked plum in a suri-bachi and grind to a fine powder. Place about 1 teaspoon powder in a cup and pour 1 cup of hot water over it. Mix and drink while warm.

Specific Dishes

Light Miso Soup

2 cups water
¼ cup wakame, soaked and sliced
½ cup onions, sliced in thin half-moons
½ tsp barley miso

Place water in a saucepan and bring to a boil. Add the wakame and simmer 1–2 minutes. Add the onions and cook 3–5 minutes, or until very soft. Reduce the flame to very low. Purée the miso with a little water or soup broth and add to the soup. Simmer 2–3 minutes. Serve garnished with a few finely sliced scallions.

Squash and Onions

> ½ cup winter squash (buttercup or Hokkaido pumpkin)
> ½ cup onions, quartered
> 1 strip kombu, 3–4 inches long, soaked and cubed
> water
> sea salt

Put the kombu in a pot. Place the onions and squash on top of the kombu. Add about ½ inch of water and a couple grains of sea salt. Bring to a boil, then cover and reduce the flame to low. Simmer until the squash is very soft, approximately 20 minutes or so.

Nori Condiment

> 2 sheets nori
> water
> tamari

Tear the nori into 1-inch squares and place in a saucepan. Add enough water to just cover the nori. Bring to a boil, then cover and reduce the flame to low. Simmer until almost all of the liquid is gone. Add a couple of drops of tamari and simmer 3–4 minutes longer.

Daikon, Daikon Leaves and Kombu

> ½ cup daikon, sliced into ½-inch-thick rounds and quartered
> ½ cup daikon greens, chopped
> 1 strip kombu, soaked and cubed
> water
> tamari

Put kombu in a saucepan. Set the daikon on top of the kombu. Add enough water to half-cover the daikon. Bring to a boil. Reduce the flame to low, cover and simmer about 30–35 minutes. Add the greens and a few drops of tamari. Simmer several minutes until the greens are done. If too much liquid remains, it may be thickened with kuzu for a sauce, or used in soup.

Pearl Barley Soup

> ½ cup pearl barley, soaked 6–8 hours
> 1 strip kombu, 2–3 inches long, soaked and diced
> ¼ cup diced onions
> 2 Tbsp diced celery
> 1 shiitake mushroom, soaked and diced
> ¼ cup diced carrots
> 3 cups water
> tamari

Place the kombu in a saucepan. Add the onions, celery, shiitake, carrots and pearl barley. Add water and bring to a boil. Cover and reduce the flame to low. Simmer about 45 minutes, until the barley is soft. Add a little tamari and continue to simmer another 10–15 minutes. Garnish with chopped parsley or scallions.

Hijiki

> ½ cup hijiki, washed, soaked and sliced
> ½ cup onions, sliced in thin half-moons
> ½ cup carrots, cut in matchsticks
> ½ cup tempeh, cubed
> water
> tamari

Place about ¼ inch of water in a skillet and bring to a boil. Add the onions and sauté 1–2 minutes. Add the carrots and tempeh. Place the hijiki on top of the tempeh. Add enough water to half-cover the hijiki and vegetables. Bring to a boil, then cover and reduce the flame to low. Simmer about 35 minutes. Season with a very small amount of tamari and continue to cook another 15–20 minutes, until almost all remaining liquid is gone.

Azuki-Kombu-Squash

$\frac{1}{4}$ cup azuki beans, washed and soaked 6–8 hours
$\frac{1}{4}$ cup winter squash (such as buttercup), cubed into 1-inch chunks
1 strip kombu, 2–3 inches long
water
sea salt

Put the kombu in a pot and add the squash chunks. Place azuki beans on top of the squash. Add water to just cover the squash. Bring to a boil, then cover and reduce the flame to low. Simmer about 1–1$\frac{1}{2}$ hours, until the beans are soft. Add a pinch of sea salt and simmer another 20–30 minutes. While the beans are cooking it will be necessary to add additional water occasionally to prevent burning. Add only enough to cover the squash but not the beans. Once the sea salt has been added it is not necessary to add any more water.

Colds and Flu ——————————————————————

■ *Special dishes and preparations:*

Soft Rice

See above recipe.

Lotus Root Tea

1 piece lotus root, 3–4 inches long
several grains of sea salt

Grate the lotus root on a fine grater. Wrap in a piece of sterile cotton cheesecloth and squeeze out the lotus juice into a measuring cup. Add an equal amount of water to the juice. Place water and juice in a saucepan, and add the sea salt. Bring to a boil, stirring constantly. Reduce the flame to low and simmer several seconds. Drink warm.

■ *Home care:*

Ume-Sho-Kuzu

See above recipe.

Warm Roasted Salt Pack

1 cup sea salt

Place the sea salt in a skillet and dry-roast several minutes on a medium-low flame. Continue until the salt turns slightly off-white and a strong chlorine smell is released. Place the hot salt in a cotton pillowcase or sack and tie shut to prevent spilling. Wrap a thick bath towel around the sack and then apply.

Earaches

■ *Home care:*

Warm Sesame Oil Drops

$\frac{1}{4}$ cup light sesame oil

Place the sesame oil in a saucepan. Turn flame to low, and heat the oil. Strain the hot oil through sterile cotton cheesecloth into a small bottle. Cover tightly to store. Place 1–2 drops of warm oil in the affected ear. (The oil can be heated by placing the jar in hot water.)

Mumps

■ *Special dishes and preparations:*

Kinpira

$\frac{1}{2}$ cup burdock, sliced in matchsticks
$\frac{1}{2}$ cup carrots, sliced in matchsticks
water
tamari

Put about $\frac{1}{4}$ inch of water in a skillet and bring to a boil. Place the burdock in the skillet and sauté for 2–3 minutes. Place the carrots on top of the burdock. Add about $\frac{1}{4}$ cup of water, cover and reduce the flame to low. Simmer until the burdock and carrots are tender, about 10 minutes. Add a small amount of tamari and continue to cook another 5 minutes. Remove cover and sauté until remaining liquid is gone.

Whooping Cough

■ *Special dishes and preparations:*

Vegetables Nishime with Lotus Root

$\frac{1}{8}$ cup celery, sliced on a thick diagonal
$\frac{1}{4}$ cup daikon, cut in chunks
$\frac{1}{2}$ cup buttercup squash, cut in chunks

¼ cup carrots, cut in chunks
¼ cup lotus root, cut in ¼-inch chunks
1 strip kombu, 2–3 inches long, soaked and cubed
water
tamari

Place the kombu in a pot. Add the celery, daikon, squash, carrots and lotus root. Add ¼–½ inch of water to the pot. Bring to a boil, cover and reduce the flame to medium-low. Simmer about 30 minutes, until all the vegetables are very soft and sweet. Add a very small amount of tamari and continue to simmer another 10 minutes, until almost all remaining liquid is gone. Mix the vegetables to coat them with any remaining liquid and then place in a serving bowl.

Arame with Lotus Root

½ cup arame, washed and sliced
½ cup onions, sliced in thin half-moons
½ cup carrots, sliced in matchsticks
¼ cup lotus root, quartered and thinly sliced
water
tamari

Heat about ¼ inch of water in a skillet. Place the onions in the hot water and water-sauté 2–3 minutes. Put the carrots and lotus root on top of the onions. Place the arame on top of the vegetables. Do not mix. Add enough cold water to almost cover the vegetables but not the arame. Cover and bring to a boil. Reduce the flame to medium-low and simmer about 30 minutes. Add a small amount of tamari and cook another 10–15 minutes. Remove the cover, turn the flame up to medium-high and cook until almost all remaining liquid is gone. Mix and serve.

Light Miso Soup with Onions and Scallions

See Light Miso Soup with Wakame and Scallions.

Broiled White-Meat Fish

Simply place a small piece of white-meat fish on a baking sheet, squeeze a little fresh lemon juice on top and add a couple of drops of tamari. Place in a broiler and cook several minutes, until the fish is soft and tender. Do not cook too long as the fish may become tough.

Fish and Vegetable Stew *(2 bowls)*

¼ cup white-meat fish (haddock, sole, schrod, etc.)
1 strip kombu, 2 inches long, soaked and diced

1 shiitake mushroom, soaked, stem removed and diced
2 cups water
1 stalk celery, diced
1 piece fresh daikon, 2 inches long, diced
1 onion, diced
1 carrot, cut in 1-inch chunks
tamari

Place kombu and shiitake in the pot. Add water and bring to a boil. Cover and reduce the flame to medium-low and simmer about 5 minutes. Add the celery, daikon, onions and carrots. Cover and simmer several minutes until the vegetables are very soft and tender. Add the fish and simmer about 5 minutes. Add tamari (very mild) and simmer another 10 minutes on a low flame.

Bed-wetting

■ *Special dishes and preparations:*

Hot Apple Cider

1 cup apple cider
1 grain sea salt

Place cider and salt in a saucepan and heat up. Remove from heat and serve warm or at room temperature.

Baked Apple

1 baking apple
water

Wash the apple and place it in a baking dish with about ⅛ inch of water. Cover and bake at 350°F. for about 30 minutes. Remove and slice or remove skin and seeds for younger child.

Applesauce

2 apples, washed, skin removed and sliced
½ cup water
small pinch of sea salt

Place water, apples and sea salt in a saucepan. Cover and bring to a boil. Reduce the flame to medium-low and simmer about 7–10 minutes, until the apples are soft and tender. Place the apples and water in a food mill and hand grind, or grind in a suribachi.

Kanten

> 1 cup apple juice
> 1 cup water
> 1 apple, sliced or skin removed and sliced
> small pinch of sea salt
> 2½–3 Tbsp agar-agar flakes (read directions on package)

Place all ingredients in a saucepan, and bring to a boil. Cover, reduce flame to low and simmer 2–3 minutes. Remove from flame and pour into a glass baking dish or ceramic bowl. To jell quickly, place in the refrigerator. Kanten can also be left out at room temperature to jell more slowly.

Pinworms

■ *Special dishes and preparations:*

Soba with Light Tamari Broth and Scallions

> 1 cup cooked and rinsed soba noodles
> 1 tsp sliced scallions
> *Broth:*
> 1 cup water
> 1 strip kombu, 1–2 inches long, soaked
> tamari

Place water and kombu in a pot. Cover and bring to a boil. Reduce the flame to low, and simmer about 7–10 minutes. Season very lightly with a couple drops of tamari and simmer about 5 minutes longer. Place rinsed noodles in the broth to warm them slightly. Place noodles and broth in a bowl and garnish with sliced scallions.

Roasted Pumpkin Seeds *(no salt)*

> ½ cup pumpkin seeds, rinsed

Heat a stainless steel skillet and add the pumpkin seeds. (Do not add any oil.) To evenly roast and prevent burning, move the seeds from side to side constantly with a wooden spoon or bamboo rice paddle. Lower the flame to medium-low. To ensure even roasting, occasionally shake the pan to bring the seeds on the bottom up to the top. Continue several minutes until the seeds begin to pop and turn golden brown. Remove immediately and place in a bowl to prevent burning.

Roasted Sunflower Seeds *(no salt)*

> ½ cup sunflower seeds, rinsed

Prepare same as for pumpkin seeds.

Roasted Squash Seeds *(no salt)*

   ½ cup squash seeds, pulp removed and washed

Spread squash seeds on a baking sheet and place in a 350°F. oven for about 20 minutes. Every few minutes stir the seeds with a wooden spoon to prevent burning and to evenly roast. When the seeds are golden brown, remove and place in a bowl to cool off. For small children the seeds can be chopped to make them easier to digest.

Corsican Sea Vegetable Tea

   2 cups water
   ¼ cup Corsican sea vegetable, rinsed

Place water and sea vegetable in a saucepan and bring to a boil. Reduce the flame to low, cover and simmer until 1 cup of liquid remains. Remove, allow to cool, and serve ¼ cup tea for children under two, ½ cup for children two to five years old, and 1 cup for children over five years old.

Warm Sesame Oil and Ginger Application

   ¼ cup sesame oil
   ¼ tsp ginger juice

Place oil in a saucepan on a low flame. Add ginger juice and heat up slowly. Remove and place in a tightly sealed glass jar to store, or, if using immediately, dip sanitized cotton into the oil and apply to the affected area.

Macrobiotic Resources

Macrobiotics International in Boston and its major educational centers in the United States, Canada, and around the world offer ongoing classes for the general public in macrobiotic cooking and traditional food preparation and natural processing. They also offer instruction in Oriental medicine, shiatsu massage, pregnancy and natural child care, yoga, meditation, science, culture and the arts, and world peace and world government activities. Macrobiotics International Educational Centers also provide way of life guidance services with trained and certified consultants, make referrals to professional health care associates, and cooperate in research and food programs in hospitals, medical schools, prisons, drug rehabilitation clinics, nursing homes, and other institutions. In scores of other cities and communities, there are smaller Macrobiotics International learning centers, residential centers, and information centers offering some classes and services.

Most of the foods mentioned in this book are available at natural foods stores, selected health food stores, and a growing number of supermarkets around the world. Macrobiotic specialty items are also available by mail order from various distributors and retailers.

Please contact Macrobiotics International in Boston or other national centers listed below for information on regional and local activities in your area, as well as whole foods outlets and mail order sources.

Global Headquarters
Macrobiotics International
Box 568
Brookline, Mass. 02147
617–738–0045

Australia
Australian Macrobiotic
  Association
1 Carlton Street, Prahran
Melbourne, 3181, Australia
03–529–1620

Belgium
Oost West Centrum
  Kushi Institute
Consciencestraat 48
Antwerpen, 2000, Belgium
03–230–13–82

Bermuda
Macrobiotic Center of
  Bermuda
In-The-Lee, Deepwood
Drive Fairyland, Pembroke,
Bermuda
809–29–5–2275

Britain
Community Health
  Foundation
188–194 Old Street London,
ECIV 9BP, England
01–251–4076

Canada
861 Queen Street
Toronto, Ontario
M6J IC4, Canada

France
Le Grain Sauvage
  Macrobiotic Association
15 Rue Letellier 75015
Paris, France
33–1–828–4773

Germany
Ost West Zentrum
Eppendorfer Marktplatz
13 D-2000 Hamburg 20
040–47–27–50

Holland
Oost West Centrum
  Kushi Institute
Achtergracht 17
1017 WL Amsterdam,
Holland
020–240–203

Hong Kong
Conduit RD. 41A,
Rome CT. 8D Hong Kong,
Hong Kong
5–495–268

Israel
24 Amos Street, Tel Aviv,
Israel
442979

Italy
Fondazione Est Ovest
Via de'Serragli 4
50124 Florence, Italy

Japan
Macrobiotics—Tokyo
20–9 Higashi Mine, Ota-ku,
Tokyo 146, Japan
03–753–9216

Lebanon
Mary Naccour
Couvent St. Elie
Box 323 Antelias
Beirut, Lebanon

Norway
East West Center
Frydenlundsgt 2 0169
Oslo 1, Norway
02–60–47–79

Portugal
Unimave
Rua Mouzinha da
Silveira 25, 1200 Lisboa,
Portugal
1–557–362

Switzerland
Ost West Zentrum
Postfach 2502 Bern,
3001 Switzerland
031–25–65–40

United Arab Emirates
Box 4943 SATWA
Dubai, United Arab
Emirates
040440–031
  (national)
97–1–44–4–0031
  (international)

United Nations
United Nations Macro-
  biotics Society
c/o Katsuhide Kitatani
U.N. Development
Programme
1 United Nations Plaza
New York, N.Y. 10017
212–906–5844

United States
Kushi Institute
17 Station Street
Brookline, Mass. 02147
617–738–0045

For those who wish to study further, the Kushi Institute, an educational institution founded in Boston in 1979 with affiliates in London, Amsterdam, Antwerp, and Florence, offers full- and part-time instruction for individuals who wish to become trained and certified macrobiotic cooking instructors, teachers, and counselors. The Kushi Institute publishes a *Worldwide Macrobiotic Directory* every year listing Kushi Institute graduates and macrobiotic centers, friends, and businesses around the world. The Cook Instructor Service is an extension of the Kushi Institute and is comprised of specially qualified graduates of the Kushi Institute's advanced cooking program. These men and women are available to assist individuals and families in learning the basics of macrobiotic food preparation and home care in their home.

Kushi Institute and Cook Instructor Service
Box 7
Becket, Mass. 01223
413–623–5712

Ongoing developments are reported in the Kushi Foundation's periodicals, including the *East West Journal*, a monthly magazine begun in 1971 and now with an international readership of 200,000. The *EWJ* features regular articles on the macrobiotic approach to health and nutrition, as well as ecology, science, psychology, natural child care, and the arts. In each issue there is a macrobiotic cooking column and articles on traditional food cultivation and natural foods processing.

East West Journal
17 Station St.
Brookline, Massachusetts 02146
617–232–1000

Recommended Reading

Books

Aihara, Cornellia. *The Dō of Cooking.* Chico, Calif.: George Ohsawa Macrobiotic Foundation, 1972.

———. *Macrobiotic Childcare.* Oroville, Calif.: George Ohsawa Macrobiotic Foundation, 1971.

Aihara, Herman. *Basic Macrobiotics.* Tokyo & New York: Japan Publications, Inc., 1985.

American Red Cross. *Standard First Aid and Personal Safety.* Garden City, New York: Doubleday and Company, 1979.

Brown, Virginia, with Susan Stayman. *Macrobiotic Miracle: How A Vermont Family Overcame Cancer.* Tokyo & New York: Japan Publications, Inc., 1985.

Child Health Encyclopedia. Boston: The Boston Children's Medical Center, 1975.

Dick-Read, Grantly, M. D. *Childbirth Without Fear.* New York: Harper and Row, 1944.

Dietary Goals for the United States. Washington, D. C.: Select Committee on Nutrition and Human Needs, U.S. Senate, 1977.

Diet, Nutrition, and Cancer. Washington, D. C.: National Academy of Sciences, 1982.

Dufty, William. *Sugar Blues.* New York: Warner, 1975.

East West Journal. *Natural Childcare.* Brookline, Mass.: East West Journal, 1985.

Esko, Edward and Wendy. *Macrobiotic Cooking for Everyone.* Tokyo & New York: Japan Publications, Inc., 1980.

Esko, Wendy. *Introducing Macrobiotic Cooking.* Tokyo & New York: Japan Publications, Inc., 1978.

Feinberg, Alice. *Macrobiotic Pregnancy.* Oroville, Calif.: George Ohsawa Macrobiotic Foundation, 1973.

Fukuoka, Masanobu. *The Natural Way of Farming.* Tokyo & New York: Japan Publications, Inc., 1985.

———. *The One-Straw Revolution.* Emmaus, Pa.: Rodale Press, 1978.

Gilbert, Margaret Shea. *Biography of the Unborn.* New York: Hafner Press, 1962.

Healthy People: The Surgeon General's Report on Health Promotion and Disease Prevention. Washington, D. C.: Government Printing Office, 1979.

Hippocrates. *Hippocratic Writings.* Edited by G. E. R. Lloyd. Translated by J. Chadwick and W. N. Mann. New York: Penguin Books, 1978.

I Ching or Book of Changes. Translated by Richard Wilhelm and Cary F. Baynes. Princeton: Bollingen Foundation, 1950.

Ineson, John. *The Way of Life: Macrobiotics and the Spirit of Christianity.* Tokyo & New York: Japan Publications, Inc., 1986.

Jacobs, Leonard and Barbara. *Cooking with Seitan.* Tokyo & New York: Japan Publications, Inc., 1986.

Jacobson, Michael. *The Changing American Diet.* Washington, D. C.: Center for Science in the Public Interest, 1978.

Kaibara, Ekiken. *Yojokun: Japanese Secrets of Good Health.* Tokyo: Tokuma Shoten, 1974.

Kidder, Ralph D. and Kelley, Edward F. *Choice for Survival: The Baby Boomer's Dilemma.* Tokyo & New York: Japan Publications, Inc., 1986.

Kohler, Jean and Mary Alice. *Healing Miracles from Macrobiotics.* West Nyack, N. Y.: Parker, 1979.

Kotsch, Ronald. *Macrobiotics: Yesterday and Today.* Tokyo & New York: Japan Publications, Inc., 1985.

Kushi, Aveline. *How to Cook with Miso.* Tokyo & New York: Japan Publications, Inc., 1978.

———. *Lessons of Night and Day.* Wayne, New Jersey: Avery Publishing Group, 1985.

———. *Macrobiotic Food and Cooking Series: Diabetes and Hypoglycemia; Allergies.* Tokyo & New York: Japan Publications, Inc., 1985.

———. *Macrobiotic Food and Cooking Series: Obesity, Weight Loss, and Eating Disorders; Infertility and Reproductive Disorders.* Tokyo & New York: Japan Publications, Inc., 1986.

Kushi, Aveline, with Alex Jack. *Aveline Kushi's Complete Guide to Macrobiotic Cooking.* New York: Warner Books, 1985.

Kushi, Aveline and Michio. *Macrobiotic Pregnancy and Care of the Newborn.* Edited by Edward and Wendy Esko. Tokyo & New York: Japan Publications, Inc., 1984.

Kushi, Aveline, and Wendy Esko. *The Changing Seasons Macrobiotic Cookbook.* Wayne, N. J.: Avery Publishing Group, 1983.

———. *Macrobiotic Family Favorites: Cooking for Healthy Children.* Tokyo & New York: Japan Publications, Inc., 1986.

Kushi, Aveline, with Wendy Esko. *The Macrobiotic Cancer Prevention Cookbook.* Wayne, New Jersey: Avery Publishing Group, 1986.

Kushi, Michio. *The Book of Dō-In: Exercise for Physical and Spiritual Development.* Tokyo & New York: Japan Publications, Inc., 1979.

———. *The Book of Macrobiotics.* Tokyo & New York: Japan Publications, Inc., 1977.

———. *Cancer and Heart Disease: The Macrobiotic Approach to Degenerative Disorders.* Tokyo & New York: Japan Publications, Inc., 1986 (Rev. ed.).

———. *The Era of Humanity.* Brookline, Mass.: East West Journal, 1980.

———. *How to See Your Health: The Book of Oriental Diagnosis.* Tokyo & New York: Japan Publications, Inc., 1980.

———. *Macrobiotic Health Education Series: Diabetes and Hypoglycemia; Allergies.* Tokyo & New York: Japan Publications, Inc., 1985.

———. *Macrobiotic Health Education Series: Obesity, Weight Loss, and Eating Disorders; Infertility and Reproductive Disorders.* Tokyo & New York: Japan Publications, Inc., 1986.

———. *Natural Healing through Macrobiotics.* Tokyo & New York: Japan Publications, Inc., 1978.

———. *On the Greater View: Collected Thoughts on Macrobiotics and Humanity.* Wayne, New Jersey: Avery Publishing Group, 1985.

———. *Your Face Never Lies.* Wayne, N. J.: Avery Publishing Group, 1983.

Kushi, Michio, and Alex Jack. *The Cancer Prevention Diet.* New York: St. Martin's Press, 1983.

———. *Diet for a Strong Heart.* New York: St. Martin's Press, 1984.

Kushi, Michio, with Alex Jack. *One Peaceful World*. New York: St. Martin's Press, 1986.

Kushi, Michio and Aveline. *The Macrobiotic Diet*. Tokyo & New York: Japan Publications, Inc., 1985.

Kushi, Michio, and the East West Foundation. *The Macrobiotic Approach to Cancer*. Wayne, N. J.: Avery Publishing Group, 1982.

Kushi, Michio, with Phillip Jannetta. *Macrobiotics and Oriental Medicine*. Tokyo & New York: Japan Publications, Inc., 1986.

Kushi, Michio, with Stephen Blauer. *The Macrobiotic Way*. Wayne, New Jersey: Avery Publishing Group, 1985.

Mendelsohn, Robert S., M. D. *Confessions of a Medical Heretic*. Chicago: Contemporary Books, 1979.

———. *How to Raise a Healthy Child in Spite of Your Doctor*. Chicago: Contemporary Books, 1984.

———. *Male Practice*. Chicago: Contemporary Books, 1980.

Nussbaum, Elaine. *Recovery: From Cancer to Health through Macrobiotics*. Tokyo & New York: Japan Publications, Inc., 1986.

Ohsawa, George. *Cancer and the Philosophy of the Far East*. Oroville, Calif.: George Ohsawa Macrobiotic Foundation, 1971 edition.

———. *You Are All Sanpaku*. Edited by William Dufty, New York: University Books, 1965.

———. *Zen Macrobiotics*. Los Angeles: Ohsawa Foundation, 1965.

Pregnancy, Birth and the Newborn Baby. Boston: The Boston Children's Medical Center, 1972.

Price, Weston, A., D. D. S. *Nutrition and Physical Degeneration*. Santa Monica, Calif.: Price-Pottenger Nutritional Foundation, 1945.

Pryor, Karen. *Nursing Your Baby*. New York: Harper and Row, 1973.

Samuels, Mike, M. D., and Nancy. *The Well Baby Book*. New York: Summit Books, 1979.

———. *The Well Child Book*. New York: Summit Books, 1982.

Sattilaro, Anthony, M. D., with Tom Monte. *Recalled by Life: The Story of My Recovery from Cancer*. Boston: Houghton-Mifflin, 1982.

Scott, Neil E., with Jean Farmer. *Eating with Angels*. Tokyo & New York: Japan Publications, Inc., 1986.

Spock, Benjamin, M. D. *Baby and Child Care*. New York: Pocket Books, 1976.

Tara, William. *A Challenge to Medicine*. Tokyo & New York: Japan Publications, Inc., 1986.

———. *Macrobiotics and Human Behavior*. Tokyo & New York: Japan Publications, Inc., 1985.

Taylor, John F. *The Hyperactive Child and the Family*. New York: Dodd, Mead, and Company, 1980.

Yamamoto, Shizuko. *Barefoot Shiatsu*. Tokyo & New York: Japan Publications, Inc. 1979.

The Yellow Emperor's Classic of Internal Medicine. Translated by Ilza Veith, Berkeley: University of California Press, 1949.

Periodicals

East West Journal. Brookline, Mass.
Macromuse. Washington, D. C.
Nutrition Action. Washington, D. C.
"The People's Doctor" by Robert S. Mendelsohn, M. D. and Marian Tompson,
    Evanston, Ill.

About the Authors and Editors

Michio Kushi was born in Kokawa, Wakayama-ken, Japan in 1926. In 1949, after studies in political science and international law at Tokyo University, he came to the United States. Inspired by George Ohsawa's dietary teachings, he began his lifelong study of the application of traditional philosophy and medicine to solving the problems of the modern world.

In the early 1960s, Michio Kushi and his family moved to Boston from New York and founded Erewhon, the nation's pioneer natural foods distributor, to make organically grown whole foods and naturally processed foods available. During the last twenty years, he has lectured around the world on diet, health, philosophy, and culture and given personal dietary and way of life counseling to thousands of individuals and families. In 1971 his students founded the *East West Journal* to provide macrobiotic information, and in 1972 the East West Foundation was started to spread macrobiotic education and research. Today there are about 500 local and regional macrobiotic centers throughout the United States, Canada, and Europe and in parts of Latin America, the Middle East, Asia, and Australia. In 1978 Michio and Aveline Kushi founded the Kushi Institute, an educational organization for the training of macrobiotic teachers, counselors, and cooks, with affiliates in London, Amsterdam, Antwerp, Florence, Paris, and Barcelona. As a further means toward addressing problems of world health and world peace, the Kushis established Macrobiotic Congresses of North America, Europe, and the Caribbean which meet annually.

In recent years, Michio Kushi has met with government and social leaders at the United Nations, the World Health Organization, the White House, and many foreign capitals. His seminars and lectures on a dietary approach to cancer, heart disease, AIDS, and other disorders have attracted thousands of doctors, nurses, nutritionists, and other health care professionals. Medical researchers at Harvard Medical School, Tulane University, the University of Minnesota School of Public Health, Ghent University, and other universities, hospitals, prisons, and schools are currently pursuing research on the effectiveness of the macrobiotic diet. In 1985 he was elected general president of the International Confederation of Natural Medicine Associations, an association of 300 natural medical and health care organizations with international headquarters in Madrid, Spain.

Michio Kushi has published over a dozen books including *The Book of Macrobiotics*, *How to See Your Health: The Book of Oriental Diagnosis*, *Natural Healing through Macrobiotics*, *The Cancer-Prevention Diet*, and *Diet for a Strong Heart*. He lives with his wife Aveline and several of their children in Brookline, Massachusetts, and has a retreat center in Becket, Massachusetts, located in the lovely Berkshire Mountains.

Aveline Kushi was born in 1923 in a small mountain village in the Izumo area of Japan. At college she was a star gymnast, but her athletic career was cut short by World War II. During the war she taught elementary school in her mountain district and after the war became involved in world peace activities at the Student World Government Association near Tokyo directed by George Ohsawa. In 1951 she came to the United States and married Michio Kushi. Along with her husband, she has devoted her life to spreading macrobiotics. As co-founder of Erewhon, the *East West Journal*, the East West Foundation, the Kushi Institute, and the Kushi Foundation, she has taken an active role in macrobiotic education and development.

During the last twenty years in the Boston area, many thousands of young people have visited and studied at her home in order to change their way of life in a more natural direction. She has given countless seminars on macrobiotic cooking, pregnancy and child care, and medicinal cooking for cancer, heart disease, and AIDS patients. She has been instrumental in arranging visits to the United States by teachers and performers of such traditional arts as the Tea Ceremony, Noh Drama, and Buddhist meditation.

Aveline has written and illustrated several books including *How to Cook with Miso*, *The Changing Seasons Cookbook*, and *Aveline Kushi's Complete Guide to Macrobiotic Cooking for Health, Harmony, and Peace*. The mother of five children and the grandmother of five, she resides in Brookline and Becket, Massachusetts, and with her husband spends about half the year teaching abroad.

Edward and Wendy Esko have practiced and taught macrobiotics for more than fifteen years. Edward was born in Philadelphia in 1950. He studied communications and business at Temple University, and gained a reputation as a songwriter and performer before moving to Boston to study with the Kushis in 1972. Wendy was born in upstate New York in 1949, and began macrobiotic studies in Boston in 1973. Edward and Wendy helped pioneer macrobiotic educational programs in the 1970s, including annual summer study programs at Amherst College and the first of the Kushi's European seminars. They also organized the East West Foundation's annual conferences on the Macrobiotic Approach to Cancer, and edited Mr. Kushi's earliest publications on cancer and diet. They have authored or edited several popular books, including *Introducing Macrobiotic Cooking, Macrobiotic Cooking for Everyone, The Changing Seasons Macrobiotic Cookbook*, and *Natural Healing through Macrobiotics*. They are also active in helping new authors develop macrobiotic publishing projects. They live with their five children in Becket, Massachusetts, and teach at the Kushi Institute, as well as throughout the United States and internationally.

Index